D0054126

"Why, Brown, is that you?" she quavered.—Page 76.

SPECIAL LIMITED EDITION

THE
LIGHTNING CONDUCTOR

THE STRANGE ADVENTURES OF A MOTOR-CAR

EDITED BY

C. N. and A. M. WILLIAMSON

Authors of " The Princess Passes "

REVISED, ENLARGED
AND ILLUSTRATED

GROSSET & DUNLAP

NEW YORK

TO THE REAL MONTIE

THE LIGHTNING CONDUCTOR

MOLLY RANDOLPH TO HER FATHER

In the Oak Room, the "White Lion,"
Cobham, Surrey, *November* 12.

Dear Shiny-headed Angel,

I hope you won't mind, but I've changed all
my plans. I've bought an automobile, or a motor-
car, as they call it over here; and while I'm writing
to you, Aunt Mary is having nervous prostration on
a sofa in a corner at least a hundred years old—I
mean the sofa, not the corner, which is a good deal
more. But perhaps I'd better explain.

Well, to begin with, some people we met on the
steamer (they were an archdeacon, with charming
silk legs, and an archdeaconess who snubbed us till
it leaked out through that Aunt Mary that you were
the Chauncey Randolph) said if we wanted to see a
thoroughly characteristic English village, we ought
to run out to Cobham; and we ran—to-day.

Aunt Mary had one of her presentiments against
the expedition, so I was sure it would turn out nice.
When we drove up to this lovely old red-brick hotel,
in a thing they call a fly because it crawls; there were
several automobiles starting off, and I can tell you I
felt small—just as if I were Miss Noah getting out the
ark. (Were there any Miss Noahs, by the way?)

One of the automobiles was different from any I've ever seen on our side or this. It was high and dignified, like a chariot, and looked over the heads of the others as the archdeaconess used to look over mine till she heard whose daughter I was. A *chauffeur* was sitting on the front seat, and a gorgeous man had jumped down and was giving him directions. He wasn't looking my way, so I seized the opportunity to snapshot him, as a souvenir of English scenery; but that tactless Kodak of mine gave the loudest "click" you ever heard, and he turned his head in time to suspect what had been happening. I swept past with my most "haughty Lady Gwendolen" air, talking to Aunt Mary, and hoped I shouldn't see him again. But we'd hardly got seated for lunch in a beautiful old room, panelled from floor to ceiling with ancient oak, when he came into the room, and Aunt Mary, who has a sneaking weakness for titles (I suppose it's the effect of the English climate), murmured that *there* was her ideal of a duke.

The Gorgeous Man strolled up and took a place at our table. He passed Aunt Mary some things which she didn't want, and then began to throw out a few conversational feelers. If you're a girl, and want fun in England, it's no end of a pull being American; for if you do anything that people think queer, they just sigh, and say, "Poor creature! she's one of those mad Americans," and put you down as harmless. I don't know whether an English girl would have talked or not, but I did; and he knew lots of our friends, especially in Paris, and it was easy to see he was a raving, tearing "swell," even if he wasn't exactly a duke. I can't remember how it began, but *really* it was Aunt Mary and not I who chattered about our trip, and how we were abroad for the first time, and were going to "do" Europe as soon as we had "done" England.

The Gorgeous Man had lived in France (he seems to have lived nearly everywhere, and to know everybody and everything worth knowing), and, said he, "What a pity we couldn't do our tour on a motor-car!" At that I became flippant, and inquired which, in his opinion, would be more suitable as *chauffeur*— Aunt Mary or I; whereupon he announced that he was not joking, but serious. We ought to have a motor-car and a *chauffeur*. Then we might say, like Monte Cristo, "The world is mine."

He went on to tell of the wonderful journeys he'd made in his car, "which we might have noticed outside." It seemed it was better than any other sort of car in the world; in fact there was no other exactly like it, as it had been made especially for him. You simply couldn't break it, it was so strong; the engine would outlast two of any other kind; and one of the advantages was that it had belts and a marvellous arrangement called a "jockey pulley" to regulate the speed: consequently it ran more "sweetly" (that was the word he used) than gear-driven cars, which, according to him, jerk, and are noisy, break easily, and do all sorts of disagreeable things.

By the time we were half through lunch I was envying him his car, and feeling as if life wasn't worth living, because I couldn't have it to play with. I asked if I could buy one like it, but he was very discouraging. He had had his fitted up with lots of expensive improvements, and it didn't pày the firm to make cars like that for the public, so I would have to order one specially, and it might be months before it could be delivered. I was thinking it rather inconsiderate in him to work me up to such a pitch, just to cast me down again, when he mentioned, in an incidental way, that he intended to sell his car, because he had ordered a racer of forty horse-power.

I jumped at that and said, "Why not sell it to me?"

You *ought* to have seen Aunt Mary's face! But we didn't give her time to speak, and gasps are more effectual as punctuations than interruptions.

Her Duke was too much moved to pause for them. He hurried to say that he hoped I hadn't misunderstood him. The last thought in his mind had been to "make a deal." Of course, if I really contemplated buying a car, I must see a great many different kinds before deciding. But as it seemed I had never had a ride on an automobile (*your* fault, Dad—your only one!), he would be delighted to take us a little spin in his car.

Before Aunt Mary could get in a word I had accepted; for I *did* want to go. And what is Aunt Mary for if not to make all the things I want to do and otherwise couldn't, strictly proper?

Anyhow, we went, and it was heavenly. I know how a bird feels now, only more so. You know, Dad, how quickly I make up my mind. I take that from you, and in our spin through beautiful lanes to a delightful hotel called—just think of it!—the "Hautboy and Fiddle," at the village of Ockham, I'd had quite time enough to determine that I wanted the Duke's car, if it could be got.

I said so; he objected. You've no idea how delicate he was about it, so afraid it might seem that he had taken advantage. I assured him that, if anything, it was the other way round, and at last he yielded. The car really is a beauty. You can put a big trunk on behind, and there are places for tools and books and lunch, and no end of little things, in a box under the cushions we sit on, and even under the floor. You never saw anything so convenient. He showed me everything, and explained the machinery, but that part I forgot as fast as he talked, so I can't tell you now exactly on what principle the engine works. When it came to a talk about price I thought he would say two thousand five hundred dollars at least (that's five hundred pounds, isn't it?) for such a splendid chariot. I know Jimmy Payne gave nearly twice that for the one he brought over to New York last year, and it wasn't half as handsome; but—would you believe it?—the man seemed quite shy at naming one thousand five hundred dollars. It was a second-hand car now, he insisted, though he had only had it three months, and he wouldn't think of charging more. I felt as if I were playing the poor fellow a real Yankee trick when I cried "Done!"

Well, now, Dad, there's my confession. That's all up to date, except that the Duke, who isn't a duke, but plain Mr. Reginald Cecil-Lanstown ("plain" seems hardly the word for all that, does it?) is to bring *my* car, late his, to Claridge's on Monday, and I'm to pay. You dear, to have given me such an unlimited letter of credit! He's got to get me a *chauffeur* who can speak French and knows the Continent, and Aunt Mary and I will do the rest of our London shopping on an automobile—my own, if you please. Then, when we are ready to cross the Channel, we'll drive to Newhaven, ship the car to Dieppe, and after that I hope we shan't so much as *see* a railroad train, except from a long distance. Automobiles for ever, say I, mine in particular.

I'm writing this after we have come back to Cobham, and while we wait for the fly which is to take us to the station. Aunt Mary says I am mad. She is quite "off" her Duke now, and thinks he is a fraud. By the way, when that photo is developed I'll send it to you, so that you can see your daughter's new gee-gee. Here comes the cab, so good-bye, you old saint. From

Your sinner,

MOLLY.

Dearest,

I've got it; it's mine; bought and paid for.
It's so handsome that even Aunt Mary is mollified.
(I didn't mean that for a *pun*, but let it pass.) Mr.
Cecil-Lanstown has told me everything I ought to
know (about motor-cars, I mean), and now, after
having tea with us, looking dukier than ever, he has
departed with a roll of your hard-earned money in
his pocket. It's lucky I met him when I did, and
secured the car, for he has been called out of England
on business, is going to-morrow, and seems not to
know when he'll be able to get back. But he says
we may meet in France when he has his big racing
automobile.

The only drawback to my new toy is the *chauffeur*.
Why "*chauffeur*," by the way, I wonder? He doesn't
heat anything. On the contrary, if I understand the
matter, it's apparently his duty to keep things cool,
including his own head. This one looks as if he had
had his head on ice for years. He is the gloomiest
man I ever saw, gives you the feeling that he may
burst into tears any minute; but Mr. Cecil-Lanstown says he is one of the best *chauffeurs* in England,
and thoroughly understands this particular make of
car, which is German.

The man's name is Rattray.   It suits him somehow.
If I were the heroine of a melodrama, I should feel
the minute I set eyes on Rattray that he was the
villain of the piece, and I should hang on like grim
death to any marriage certificates or wills that might
concern me, for I should know it would be his aim
during at least four acts to get possession of them.
He has enormous blue eyes like Easter eggs, and his
ears look something like cactuses, only, thank goodness, I'm spared their being green; they wouldn't go
with his complexion.   I talked to him and put on
scientific airs, but I'm afraid they weren't effective.
for he hardly said anything, only looked gloomy, and
as if he read "amateur" written on my soul or somewhere where it wasn't supposed to show.   He's gone
now to make arrangements for keeping *my* car in a
garage.   He's to bring it round every morning at ten
o'clock, and is to teach me to drive.   I won't seal
this letter up till to-morrow then I can tell you how
I like my first lesson.

November 15.

I *was* proud of the car when I went out on it
yesterday.   Aunt Mary wouldn't go, because she
doesn't wish to be the "victim of an experiment."
Rattray drove for a long way, but when we got
beyond the traffic, towards Richmond, I took his
place, and my lesson began.   It's harder than I
thought it would be, because you have to do so many
things at once.   You really ought to have three or
four hands with this car, Rattray says.   When I

asked him if it was different with other cars, he
didn't seem to hear. Already I've noticed that he's
subject to a sort of spasmodic deafness, but I suppose
I must put up with that, as he is such a fine mechanic.
One can't have everything.

With your left hand you have to steer the car by
means of a kind of tiller, and to this is attached the
horn to warn creatures of all sorts that you're coming.
I blow this with my right hand, but Rattray says I
ought to learn to do it while steering with the left, as
there are quantities of other things to be done with
the right hand. First there is a funny little handle
with which you change speeds whenever you come
to a hill; then there is the "jockey-pulley-lever,"
which gives the right tension to the belts (this is
very important); the "throttle-valve-lever," on which
you must always keep your hand to control the
speed of the car; and the brake which you jam on
when you want to stop. So there are two things to
do with the left hand, and four things with the right,
and often most of these things must be done at the
same time. No wonder I was confused and got my
hands a little mixed, so that I forgot which was
which, and things went wrong for a second! Just
then a cart was rude enough to come round a corner.
I tried to steer to the right, but went to the left—
and you can't *think* how many things can happen
with a motor-car in one second.

Now, don't be worried! I wasn't hurt a bit; only
we charged on to the sidewalk, and butted into a
shop. It was my fault, not a bit the car's. If it
weren't a *splendid* car it would have been smashed to

pieces, and perhaps we with it, instead of just breaking the front—oh, and the shop too, a little. I shall have to pay the man something. He's a "haberdasher," whatever that is, but it *sounds* like the sort of name he might have called me if he'd been very angry when I broke his window.

The one bad consequence of my stupidity is that the poor, innocent, sinned-against car must lie up for repairs. Rattray says they may take some days. In that case Aunt Mary and I must do our shopping in a hired brougham—such an anti-climax; but Rattray *promises* that the dear thing shall be ready for our start to France on the 19th. Meanwhile, I shall console myself for my disappointment by buying an outfit for a trip—a warm coat, and a mask, and a hood, and all sorts of tricky little things I've marked in a perfectly thrilling catalogue.

Now, if you fuss, I shall be sorry I've told you the truth. Remember the axiom about the bad penny. That's

Your

MOLLY.

THE HORRIBLE RESTAURANT OF THE BOULE D'OR,
SURESNES, NEAR PARIS,

November 28.

Forgive me, dear, long - suffering - because - you - couldn't-help-yourself-Dad, for being such a beast about writing. But I did send you three cables, didn't I? Aunt Mary would have written, only I threatened her with unspeakable things if she did. I knew so well what she would say, and I wouldn't have it. Now, however, I'm going to tell you the truth, the whole truth, and nothing but the truth—no varnish. Indeed, there isn't much varnish left on anything.

I wonder if I can make you comprehend the things I've gone through in the last two or three days? Why, Dad, I feel old enough to be your mother. But I'll try and begin at the beginning, though it seems, to look back, almost before the memory of man, to say nothing of woman. Let me see, where *is* the beginning, when I was still young and happy? Perhaps it's in our outfit for the trip. I can dwell upon that with comparative calmness.

Even Aunt Mary was happy. You would have had to rush out and take your "apoplectic medicine," as I used to call it, if you could have seen her trying different kinds of masks and goggles, and asking gravely which were most becoming. Thank Heaven that I've inherited your sense of humour! To that I have owed my sanity during the last *dies iræ.* (Is that the way to spell it?)

I wouldn't have the conventional kind of mask, nor goggles. Seeing Aunt Mary in her armour saved me from that. I bought what they call a "toilet mask," which women vainer than I wear at night to preserve their complexions. This was only for a last resort on very dusty days, to be hidden from sight by a thin, grey veil, as if I were a modern prophet of Korassan.

We got dust-grey cloaks, waterproof cloth on the outside, and lined with fur. Aunt Mary invested in a kind of patent helmet, with curtains that unfurl on the sides, to cover the ears; and I found myself so fetching in a hood that I bought one, as well as a toque, to provide for all weathers. Then we got a fascinating tea-basket, foot-warmers that burn charcoal, and had two flat trunks made on purpose to fit the back of the car, with tarpaulin covers to take on and off. Our big luggage we planned to send to places where we wanted to make a long stay; but we would have enough with us to make us feel self-contained and independent.

We did look ship-shape when we started from the "Carlton" on the morning of November 19th, with our luggage strapped on behind, the foot-warmers and tea-basket on the floor, our umbrellas in a hanging-basket contrivance, a fur-lined waterproof rug over Aunt Mary's knees and mine. I'd taken no more lessons since that first day I wrote you about, owing to the car not being ready until the night before our start, so Rattray sat in front alone, Aunt Mary and I together behind.

We meant to have got off about eight, as we had to drive over fifty miles to Newhaven, where the car was to be shipped that night; but Rattray had a little difficulty in starting the car, and we were half an hour late, which was irritating, especially as a good many people were waiting to see us off. At last, however, we shot away in fine style, which checked Aunt Mary in the middle of her thirty-second sigh.

All went well for a couple of hours. We were out in the country—lovely undulating English country. The car, which Mr. Cecil-Lanstown had said was beyond all others as a hill-climber, was justifying its reputation, as I had confidently expected it would. The air was cold, but instead of making one shiver, our blood tingled with exhilaration as we flew along. You know what a chilly body Aunt Mary is? Even she didn't complain of the weather, and hardly needed her foot-warmer "This is life!" said I to myself. It seemed to me that I'd never known the height of physical pleasure until I'd driven in a motor-car. It was better than dancing on a perfect floor with a perfect partner to *plu*perfect music; better than eating when you're awfully hungry; better than holding out your hands to a fire when they're numb with cold; better than a bath after a hot, dusty railway journey. I can't give it higher praise, can I?—and I *did* wish for you. I thought you would be converted. Oh, my *un*prophetic soul!

Suddenly, sailing up a steep hill at about ten miles an hour, the car stopped, and would have run back if Rattray hadn't put on the brakes. "What's the matter?" said I, while Aunt Mary convulsively clutched my arm.

"Only a belt broken, miss," he returned gloomily. "Means twenty minutes' delay, that's all. Sorry I must trouble you ladies to get up. New belts and belt-fasteners under your seat. Tools under the floor."

We were relieved to think it was no worse, and reminded ourselves that we had much to be thankful for, while we disarranged our comfortably established selves. There were the tea-basket and the foot-warmers to be lifted from the floor and deposited on Rattray's vacant front seat, the big rug to be got rid of, our feet to be put up while the floor-board was lifted, then we had to stand while the cushions were pulled off the seat and the lid of the box raised. We, or at least I, tried to think it was part of the fun; but it was a *little* depressing to hear Rattray grunting and grumbling to himself as he unstrapped the luggage, hoisted it off the back of the car so that he could get at the broken belt inside, and plumped it down viciously on the dusty road.

The delay was nearer half an hour than twenty minutes, and it seemed extra long because it was a strain entertaining Aunt Mary to keep her from saying "I told you so!" But we had not gone two miles before our little annoyance was forgotten. That is the queer part about automobiling. You're so happy when all's going well that you forget past

"WE ATE AT A LOVELY ENGLISH INN."

misadventures, and feel joyously hopeful that you will never have any more.

We got on all right until after lunch, which we ate at a lovely inn close to George Meredith's house. Then it took half an hour to start the car again. Rattray looked as if he were going to burst. Just to watch him turning that handle in vain made me feel as if elephants had walked over me. He said the trouble was that "the compression was too strong," and that there was "back-firing"—whatever that means. Just as I was giving up hope the engine started off with a rush, and we were on the way again through the most soothingly pretty country. About four o'clock, in the midst of a glorious spin, there was a "r-r-r-tch," the car swerved to one side, Aunt Mary screamed, and we stopped dead. "Chain broken," snarled Rattray.

Up we had to jump once more: tea-basket, foot-warmers, rugs, ourselves, everything had to be hustled out of the way for Rattray to get at the tools and spare chains which we carried in the box under our seats. I began to think perhaps the car *wasn't* quite so conveniently arranged for touring as I had fancied, but I'd have died sooner than say so—then. I pretended that this was a capital opportunity for tea, so opened the tea-basket, and we had quite a picnic by the roadside while Rattray fussed with the chain. It wasn't very cold, and I looked forward to many similar delightful halts in a warmer climate "by the banks of the brimming Loire," as I put it jauntily to Aunt Mary. But she only said, "I'm sure I hope so, my dear," in a tone more chilling than the weather.

It was at least half an hour before Rattray had the
chain properly fixed, and then there was the usual
difficulty in starting. Once the handle flew round
and struck him on the back of the hand. He yelled,
kicked one of the wheels, and went to the grassy side
of the road, where in the dusk I could dimly see him
holding his hand to his mouth and rocking backwards
and forwards. He did look so like a distracted goblin
that I could hardly steady my voice to ask if he was
much hurt. "Nearly broke my hand, that's all, miss,"
he growled. At last he flew at the terrible handle
again, managed to start the motor, and we were off.

Going up a hill in a town that Rattray said was
called Lewes, I noticed that the car didn't seem to
travel with its customary springy vigour. "Loss of
power," Rattray jerked at me over his shoulder when
I questioned him as to what was the matter, and
there I had to leave it, wondering vaguely what he
meant. I think he lost the way in Lewes (it was
now quite dark, with no stars); anyhow, we made
many windings, and at last came out into a plain
between dim, chalky hills, with a shining river faintly
visible. Aunt Mary had relapsed into expressive
silence; the car seemed to crawl like a wounded
thing; but at last we got to Newhaven pier, and had
our luggage carried on board the boat. Rattray was
to follow with the car in the cargo-boat. So ended
the "lesson for the first day"—a ten-hour lesson—
and I felt sadder as well as wiser for it.

Aunt Mary went to sleep as soon as we got on the
boat; but I was so excited at the thought of seeing
France that I stayed on deck, wrapped in the warm

coat I'd bought for the car. We had a splendid
crossing, and as we got near Dieppe I could see chalk
cliffs and a great gaunt crucifix on the pier leading
into the harbour. It seemed as if I were in a dream
when I heard people chattering French quite as a
matter of course to each other, and I liked the
douaniers, the smart soldiers, and the railway porters
in blue blouses. It was four in the morning when
we landed. Of course, it was the dead season at
Dieppe, but we got in at a hotel close to the sea.
It was lovely waking up, rather late, one's very first
day in France, looking out of the window at the
bright water and the little fishing-boats, with their
red-brown sails, and smelling a really heavenly scent
of strong coffee and fresh-baked rolls.

Later in the morning I walked round to the harbour to find that the cargo-boat had arrived, and
that Rattray and the car had been landed. The
creature actually greeted me with smiles. Now
for the first time he was a comfort. He did everything, paid the deposit demanded by the custom-
house, and got the necessary papers. Then he drove
me back to the hotel, but as it was about midday I
thought that it would be nicer to start for Paris the
next day, when I hoped we could have a long, clear
run. In Paris, of course, Aunt Mary and I wanted
to stay for at least a week. Rattray promised to
thoroughly overhaul the car, so that there need be
no "incidents" on the way.

There was a crowd round us next morning—a
friendly, good-natured little crowd—when we were
getting ready to start in the stable-yard of the hotel.

Our landlady was there, a duck of a woman; the
hotel porters in green baize aprons stood and stared;
some women washing clothes at a trough in the
corner stopped their work; and a lot of funny, wee
schoolboys, with short cropped hair and black blouses
with leather belts, buzzed round, gesticulating and
trying to explain the mechanism of the car to each
other. Rattray bustled about with an oil-can in his
hand, then loaded up our luggage, and all was ready.
With more dignity than confidence I mounted to the
high seat beside Aunt Mary. This time, with one
turn of the handle, the motor started, so contrary is
this strange beast, the automobile. One day you toil
at the starting-handle half an hour, the next the thing
comes to life with a touch, and nobody can explain
why. Bowing to madame and the hotel people, we
sailed gracefully out of the hotel yard, Rattray too-
tooing a fanfarronade on the horn. It was a splendid
start!

The streets of Dieppe are of those horrid uneven
stones that the French call *pavé*, and our car jolted
over them with as much noise and clatter as if we'd
had a cargo of dishes. You see the car's very solidly
built and heavy—that, said Mr. Cecil-Lanstown, is
one of its merits. It is of oak, an inch thick, and
you can't break it. Another thing in its favour is
that it has solid tyres, and not those horrid pneu-
matics, which are always bursting and puncturing,
and give no end of trouble. " With solid tyres you
are always safe," said Mr. Cecil-Lanstown. I can't
help thinking, though, that on roads like these of
Dieppe it would be soothing to have "pneus," as they

call them. Jingle, jingle! scrunch, scrunch! goes the machinery inside, and all the loose parts of the car. It did get on my nerves.

But soon we were out of the town and on one of the smoothest roads you ever saw. Rattray said it was a "route nationale," and that they are the best roads in the world. The car bounded along as if it were on a billiard-table. Even Aunt Mary said, "Now, if it were always like *this*——" My spirits went up, up. I proudly smiled and bowed to the peasants in their orchards by the roadsides. I was even inclined to pat Rattray on the shoulder of his black leather coat. This, *this* was life! The sun shone, the fresh air sang in our ears, the car ran as if it had the strength of a giant. I felt as independent as a gipsy in his caravan, only we were travelling at many times his speed. The country seemed to unfold just like a panorama. At each turn I looked for an adventure.

We skimmed through a delicious green country given up to enormous orchards which, Aunt Mary read out of a guide-book, yield the famous *cidre de Normandie*. I thought of the lovely pink dress this land would wear by-and-by, and then suddenly we came out from a small road on to a broad, winding one, and there was a wide view over waving country, with a white town like a butterfly that had fluttered into a bird's nest. Rattray let the car go down this long road towards the valley at something like thirty miles an hour, and Aunt Mary's hand had nervously grasped the rail when there came a kind of sigh inside the car, and it paused to rest.

Rattray jumped off and made puzzled inspection. "Can't see anything wrong, miss; must take off the luggage and look inside." It is a peculiarity that every working part is hidden modestly under the body of the car. This protects them from wet and dust, Mr. Cecil-Lanstown told me; but it seems a little inconvenient to have to haul off *all* the luggage every time you want to examine the machinery. It didn't take long to find out what was the matter. The "aspiration pipe," Rattray said, had worked loose (no doubt through the jolting over the Dieppe *pavé*) and the "vapour couldn't get from the carburetter to the explosion chamber."

I only partly understood, but I felt that the poor car wasn't to blame. How could it be expected to go on without aspirating? There was "no spanner to fit the union," and Rattray darkly hinted at further trouble. Three little French boys with a go-cart had come to stare. I Kodaked them and send you their picture in this letter as a sort of punctuation to my complaints.

Well, when Rattray had screwed up the "union" as well as he could (isn't that what our statesmen did after the confederate war?), off we started again, bustled through the town in the valley (which I found from Murray was Neufchâtel-en-Bray), and had a consoling run through beautiful country until, at noon, we shot into the market-place of Forges les Eaux. It was market-day, and we drove at a walking pace through the crowded *place*, all alive with booths, the cackling of turkeys, and the lowing of cows. There seemed to be only one decent inn, and the *salle à manger* was full of loud-talking peasants, with shrewd, brown, wrinkled faces like masks, who "ate out loud," as I used to say.

The place was so thronged that Rattray had to sit at the same table with us, and though as a good democrat I oughtn't to have minded, I did squirm a little, for his manners—well, "they're better not to dwell on." But the luncheon *was* good, so French and so cheap. We hurried over it, but it took Rattray half an hour to replenish the tanks of the car with water (of course he had to lift down the luggage to do this) and to oil the bearings. We sailed out of Forges les Eaux so bravely that my hopes went up. It seemed certain we should be in Paris quite in good time, but almost as soon as we had got out of the town one of the chains glided gracefully off on to the road.

You'd think it the simplest thing in the world to slip it on again, but that was just what it wasn't. Rattray worked over it half an hour (everything takes half an hour to do on this car, I notice, when it doesn't take more), saying things under his breath which Aunt Mary was too deaf and I too dignified to hear. Finally I was driven to remark waspishly, "You'd be a bad soldier; a good soldier makes the best of things, and bears them like a man. You make the worst."

"That's all very well, miss," retorted my gloomy goblin; "but soldiers have to fight *men*, not *beasts*."

"They get killed sometimes," said I.

"There's things makes a man *want* to die," groaned he. And that silenced me, even though I heard a ceaseless mumbling about "every bloomin' screw being loose; that he'd engaged as a mechanic, not a car-maker; that if he *was* a car-maker, he was hanged if he'd disgrace himself making one of *this* sort, anyhow."

You'll think I'm exaggerating, but I vow we had not gone more than ten miles further before that chain broke again. This time I believe Rattray shed tears. As for Aunt Mary, her attitude was that of cold, Christian resignation. She had sacrificed herself to me, and would continue to do so, since such was her Duty, with a capital D; indeed, she had expected this, and from the first she had told me, etc., etc. At last the chain was forced on again and fastened with a new bolt. We sped forward for a few deceitful moments, but—detail is growing monotonous. After that something happened to the car, on the average, every hour. Chains snapped or came off; if belts didn't break, they were too short or too long. Mysterious squeaks made themselves heard; the crank-head got hot (what head wouldn't?), and we had to wait until it thought fit to cool, a process which could scarcely be accelerated by Rattray's language. He now announced that this make of car, and my specimen in particular, was *the* vilest in the automobile world. If a worse *could* be made, it did not yet exist! When I ventured to inquire why he had not expressed this opinion before leaving London, he announced that it was not his business to express opinions, but to drive such vehicles as he was engaged to drive. I hoped that there must be something wrong with the automobile which Rattray didn't understand; that in Paris I could have it put right, and that even yet all might go well. For a few miles we went with reasonable speed, and no mishaps; but half-way up a long, long hill the mystic "power" vanished once more, and there we were stranded nearly opposite a forge, from which strolled three huge, black-faced men, adorned with pitying smiles.

"Hire them to push," I said despairingly to Rattray, and as he turned a sulky back to obey, I heard a whirring sound, and an automobile flew past us up the steep hill, going about fifteen miles an hour. That did seem the last straw; and with hatred, malice, and all uncharitableness in my breast, I was shaking my fist after the thing, when it stopped politely.

There were two men in it, both in leather caps and coats—I noticed that half unconsciously. Now one of them jumped out and came walking back to us. Taking off his cap, he asked me with his eyes and Aunt Mary with his voice—in English—if there was anything he could do. He was very good-looking, and spoke nicely, like a gentleman, but he seemed so successful that I couldn't help hating him and wishing he would go away. The only thing I wanted was that he and the other man and their car should be specks in the distance when Rattray came back with his blacksmiths to push us up the hill; so I thanked him hurriedly, and said we didn't need help. Perhaps I said it rather stiffly, I was so wild to have him gone. He stood for a minute as if he would have liked to say something else, but didn't know

how, then bowed, and went back to his car. In a
minute it was shooting up hill again, and I never was
gladder at anything in my life than when I saw it
disappear over the top—only just in time too, for it
wasn't out of sight when our three blacksmiths had
their shoulders to the task.

"*There's* a good car, if you like, miss," said that
fiend Rattray. "It's a Napier. Some pleasure in
driving *that*."

I could have boxed his ears.

Once on level ground again, the car seemed to
recover a little strength. But night fell when we
were still a long way from Paris, and our poor oil-
lamps only gave light enough to make darkness
visible, so that we daren't travel at high speed.
There were uncountable belt-breakings and heart-
achings before at last, after eleven at night, we
crawled through the barriers of Paris and mounted
up the Avenue de la Grande Armée to the Arc de
Triomphe. We drove straight to the Élysée Palace
Hotel, and let Rattray take the brute beast to a
garage, which I *wished* had been a slaughter-house.

I couldn't sleep that night for thinking that I was
actually in Paris, and for puzzling what to do next,
since it was clear it would be no use going on with
the car unless some hidden ailment could be discovered and rectified. Our plan had been to stop in
Paris for a week, and then drive on to the beautiful
château country of the Loire that I've always
dreamed of seeing. Afterwards, I thought we might
go across country to the Riviera; but now, unless
light suddenly shone out of darkness, all that was

knocked on the head. What was my joy, then, in the morning, when Rattray came and deigned to inform me that he had found out the cause of the worst mischief! "The connecting-rod that worked the magnet had got out of adjustment, and so the timing of the explosions was wrong." This could be made right, and he would see to the belts and chains. In a few days we might be ready to get away, with some hope of better luck.

I was so pleased I gave him a louis. Afterwards I wished I hadn't—but that's a detail. I sent you a cable, just saying, you'll remember: "Élysée Palace for a week; all well"; and Aunt Mary and I proceeded to drown our sorrows by draughts of undiluted Paris.

Crowds of Americans were at the hotel, a good many I knew; but Aunt Mary and I kept dark about the automobile—very different from that time in London, where I was always swaggering around talking of "my motor-car" and the trip I meant to take. *Poor* little me!

Mrs. Tom van Wyck was there, and she introduced me to an Englishwoman, Lady Brighthelmstone, a viscountess, or something, and you pronounce her "Lady Brighton." She's near-sighted and looks at you through a lorgnette, which is disconcerting, and makes you feel as if your features didn't match properly; but she turned out to be rather nice, and said she hoped we'd see each other at Cannes, where she's going immediately. She expects her son to join her there. He's touring now on his motor-car, and expects to meet her and some friends on the Riviera in about a fortnight. Mrs. van Wyck told me he's the Honourable John Winston, and a very nice fellow, but I grudge him an automobile, which *goes*.

I just *couldn't* write to you that week in Paris; not that I was too busy—I'm never too busy to write to my dear old boy. But I knew you'd expect to hear how I enjoyed the trip, and I didn't want to tell you the bad news till perhaps I might have good news to add. Consequently I cabled whenever a writing-day came round.

Well, at last Rattray vowed that the car was in good condition, and we might start. It was a whole week since I'd seen the monster, and it looked so handsome as it sailed up to the hotel door that my pride in it came back. It was early in the morning, so there weren't many people about, but I shouldn't have had cause to be ashamed if there had been. We went off in fine style, and it was delicious driving through the Bois, en route for Orleans, by way of Versailles. After all, I said to myself, perhaps the car hadn't been to blame for our horrid experience. No car was perfect, even Rattray admitted that. Some little thing had gone wrong with ours, and the poor thing had been misunderstood.

We had traversed the Bois, and were mounting the long hill of Suresnes, when "squeak! squeak!" a little insinuating sound began to mingle with my reflections. I was too happy, with the sweet wind in my face, to pay attention at first, but the noise kept on, insisting on being noticed. Then it occurred to me that I'd heard it before in moments of baleful memory.

"I believe that horrid crank-head is getting hot," said I. "Are you sure it doesn't need oil?"

"Sure, miss," returned Rattray. "The crank-head's all right. That squeak ain't anything to worry about."

So I didn't worry, and we bowled along for twenty perfect minutes, then something went smash inside, and we stopped dead. It *was* the crank-head, which was nearly red hot. The crank had snapped like a carrot. I was too prostrate, and, I trust, too proud to say things to Rattray, though if he had just made sure that the lubricator was working properly, we should have been saved.

Fortunately we had lately passed a big *garage* by the Pont de Suresnes, and we "coasted" to it down the hill, although of course our engine was paralysed. You couldn't expect it to work without a head, even though that head *was* only a "crank!"

For once Rattray was somewhat subdued. He knew he was in fault, and meekly proposed to take an electric tram back to Paris, there to see if a new crank could be bought to fit, otherwise one would have to be made, and it would take two or three days. At this I remarked icily that in the latter case we would not proceed with the trip, and he could return to London. Usually he retorted, if I showed the slightest sign of disapproval, but now he merely asked if I would give him the money to buy the new crank if it were obtainable.

I had only a couple of louis in change and a five-hundred franc note, so I gave that to him, and he was to return as soon as possible, probably in an hour

and a half.   Aunt Mary and I found our way gloomily to a little third-class restaurant, where we had
coffee and things.   Time crept on and brought no
Rattray.   When two hours had passed I walked
back to the *garage*, but the proprietor had no news.
The car was standing in the place where they had
dragged it, and I climbed up to sit in gloomy state
on the back seat, feeling as if I couldn't bear to go
back to Aunt Mary until something had happened.
Then something did happen, but not the thing I had
wanted.   The very car that had stopped when we
were in trouble on the hill of the blacksmiths, far on
the other side of Paris, more than a week ago, came
gliding smoothly, deliciously into the *garage*.

The same two leather-capped and coated men
were in it, master and *chauffeur*, I thought.   The
madame of the establishment was talking sympa-
thetically to me, but I heard the voice of the man
who had asked me if he could help (the one I had
taken for the master) inquiring in French for a particular kind of essence.   Then I didn't hear any
more.   He and the *garage* man were speaking in
lower tones, and besides, the shrill condolences of
madame drowned their murmurs.   She was loudly
giving it as her opinion that my *chauffeur* had run
off with my money, and that, unless I had some
means of tracing him, I should never look upon his
face again.   I did wish that she would be quiet, at
least until the fortunate automobilists rolled away
like kings in their chariot; but I couldn't make her
stop, and I was certain they heard every word.   I
even imagined that they had deserted the subject of

petrol for my troubles, because I could see out of a
corner of an eye that the proprietor in his conversation with them nodded more than once towards my
car, in which I sat ingloriously enthroned like a sort
of captive Zenobia.

They seemed to be a long time buying their petrol,
anyway, and presently my worst fears were confirmed.
The man who had spoken to me on the fatal hill
came forward, repeating himself (like history) by
taking off his cap and wearing exactly the same
half-shy, half-interested expression as before.

He said "er" once or twice, and then informed
me that the proprietor had been telling him what
a scrape I was in, or words to that effect. He
offered to drive into Paris on his car, which would
only take a few minutes, go to the place where my
chauffeur had intended to buy the crank, see whether
he had been there, and if so, what delayed him.
Then, if anything were wrong, he would come back
and let me know.

I said that I couldn't possibly let him take so
much trouble, but he would hardly listen. He knew
the address of the place from the *garage* man, who
had recommended it to Rattray, and almost before
I knew what had happened the car and the dusty,
leather-clad men were off.

There was nothing for me to do but to go back
to Aunt Mary, which I did in no happy frame of
mind.

That Napier must have tossed its bonnet at the
legal limit of speed, for in less than an hour it drew
up before this restaurant. Out jumped *my* one of

the two men and came into the room where Aunt Mary and I had sat so long reading old French papers.

"I'm sorry to have to tell you," said he in his nice voice, "that your man appears to be a scoundrel. He hasn't been to Le Sage's, nor to another place which I tried. I'm afraid he has gone off with your money, and that your only hope of getting it will be to track the fellow with a detective."

"I don't want to track him," I said. "I never want to see him again, and I don't care about the money. I'll engage another *chauffeur*. There must be plenty in Paris."

As I said this he had rather a curious look on his face. I didn't understand it then, but I did afterwards. "I'm afraid you'll find very few who understand your make of car," he said, "which is German, and—er—perhaps not up to the very latest date."

"I can believe anything of it," said I. "But now the crank's broken, and——"

"I've taken the liberty of bringing another, which we took out of a similar car," broke in the man. "The proprietor of the *garage* across the way thinks he can put it in for you; if not, I can help him, for I once drove a car of the same make as yours, and have reason to remember it."

I burst into thanks, and when I had used up most of my prettiest adjectives I asked how long the work would take. He thought only a few hours, and my car might be ready to start again in the afternoon.

I clapped my hands at this; then I could feel my
face fall. (Funny expression, isn't it?—almost as
absurd as I "dropped my eyes"; but I think I did
that too.) "How lovely!" said I. And then, "But
what good if I can't get a *chauffeur* ?"

The man's face grew red—not a bricky, ugly red;
but as he was very brown already, it only turned
a nice mahogany colour, and made him look quite
engaging. "If you would take me," he said, "I am
at your service."

I never was more astonished in my life, and I just
sat and stared at him. I was sure he must be making
fun.

"Of course you'll think it strange," he went on in
a hurry; "but the fact is, I'm out of a job——"

"Why, are you a *real chauffeur*—a mechanic ?"
I couldn't help breaking in on him. I *almost* blurted
out that I had taken him for the master, which
would have been horrid, of course, and suddenly
I was ashamed of myself, for I had been treating
him exactly like an equal; and perhaps I was silly
enough to be a tiny bit disappointed too, for I'll
confess to you, Dad, that I'd had visions of his being
someone rather grand, which would have spread a
little jam of romance over the stale, dry bread of
this disagreeable experience. Anyhow, this man was
much better looking than his companion, whom I
knew now was the master. He wasn't a gorgeous
person, like Mr. Cecil-Lanstown, but I'd certainly
thought he had rather a distinguished air. However,
these Englishmen, even the peasants, are sometimes
such splendid types—clear-cut features, brave, keen

eyes, and all that, you know, as if their ancestors might have been Vikings.

While I was thinking, he was telling me that he was a *chauffeur*, sure enough, and that this was the last day of his engagement with his master, who didn't wish to take a mechanic any farther. His name, he said, was James Brown. He had had a good deal of experience with several kinds of cars— my sort was the first he'd ever driven; he knew it well, and if I cared to try him, he could get me a very good reference from his master, Mr. Winston.

"Mr. Winston!" I repeated. "Is your master the Honourable John Winston?"

"That is his name," he answered, though he looked so odd when he said it that I thought it wise to mention that I knew Mr. Winston's mother, so he would have a sort of warning if he weren't speaking the truth. But he didn't look like a man who would tell fibs, and to cut a long story short, he brought out a letter which the Honourable John Winston had already given him. It was very short, as if it had been written in a hurry, but nothing could have been more satisfactory. Brown, as I suppose I must call him, said that he would be able to start with us as soon as the car was ready, and when I mentioned where I wanted to go he remarked that he had been all through the château country several times on a motor-car. One can see from the way he talks that he's an intelligent, competent young man (he can't be more than twenty-eight or nine) and knows his business thoroughly. I think I'm very lucky to get him, don't you?

Now you will understand the address at the top of this long letter; and I am writing it while James Brown and the *garage* man fit the new crank into the car.   I must have been scribbling away for two hours, so almost any minute my new *chauffeur* may arrive to say that we can start.   I shall write again soon to tell you how he turns out, and all about things in general; and when I don't write I'll cable.

Your battered but hopeful
MOLLY.

FROM JACK WINSTON TO LORD LANE

My dear Montie,

I have so many things to tell you I scarcely know where to begin. First let me announce that I am in for an adventure—a real flesh and blood adventure into which I plump without premeditation, but an adventure of so delightful a kind that I hope it may continue for many a day. I know you'll say at once, "That means Woman"; and you're right. But I won't go to the heart of the story at once; I'll begin at the beginning. First, though, a word as to yourself. I miss you enormously. It is a cruel stroke of fate that you should have been ordered to Davos after you had made all your plans to go with me on my new car to the Riviera. I still think that a trip on which you would have been in the open air all day was just as likely to check incipient chest trouble as the cold dryness of Davos; but no doubt you were right to do as the doctors told you. I shall look eagerly for letters from you with bulletins of your progress. As I can't have you with me, the next best thing will be to write to you often; besides, you said that you would like to have frequent reports of my doings in France, with "plenty of detail."

Well, the new car is a stunner. I haven't so far
a fault to find with her. She takes most hills on the
third, which is very good; for though we are only
two up—Almond and I—I have luggage in the
tonneau almost equal to the weight of another
passenger. Between Dieppe and Paris she licked up
the kilometres as a running flame licks up dry wood.
She runs sweetly and with hardly any noise. The
ignition seems to work perfectly; she carries water
and petrol enough for 150 miles. I think at last
in the Napier I have found the ideal car, and you
know I have searched long enough. Almond timed
her on the level bit at Achères, and it was at the rate
of over forty-five miles an hour—not bad for a
touring car.

It was between Dieppe and Paris (somewhere
between Gisors and Meru) that the adventure began.
I was flying up a slope of perhaps one in fifteen,
when I became aware of Beauty in Distress. An
antediluvian car, which was recognisable by its
rearward protuberance as something archaic, was
stationary on the hill; two ladies sat on an extraordinarily high seat behind like a throne, and a mechanic was slouching towards a smith's forge by
the roadside. One motorist, of course, must always
offer help to another—to pass a stranded car would
be like ignoring signals of distress at sea; besides,
one of the ladies looked young and seemed to have
a charming figure. So, having passed them, I pulled
up and went back.

The ladies said "America" to me as plainly as
if they had spoken. They were most professionally

got up, the elder so befurred and goggled that I could see only the tip of her nose; the younger with a wonderfully fetching grey fur coat, a thing that I believe women call a "toque," and a double veil, which allowed only a tantalising hint of a piquant profile and a pair of bewildering grey eyes. They—or rather the younger one—met my profferred help with a rather curt refusal, but the voice that uttered it was musical to a point rare among the American women of the eastern States, and these were New York or nowhere. There was nothing for me to do except retire; but Almond, looking back as we sped away, said, "Why, sir, blowed if they haven't got those three smiths pushing them up the hill ! " From which I argued that Beauty was very jealous for the reputation of her car. This is the end of Chapter I.

Chapter II. opens at Suresnes, some days later. I was starting for Cannes, and had just crossed the bridge when, in the yard of a *garage* on the left-hand side at the foot of the hill, I detected again Beauty in Distress—the same Beauty, but a different Distress. There was the high and portly car, with Beauty perched up in it alone—Beauty in the attitude appropriate to Patience smiling at Grief. Almost before I knew what I did, I turned my car into the yard and pulled up near her, making an excuse of asking for Stelline, though, as a matter of fact, Almond had filled up the tank only half an hour before at the Automobile Club. The manager of the *garage* told me that Beauty's car was stranded with a broken crank. Now Almond had caught sight of her *mécanicien* the previous time we met,

and knew him for a wrong un in London; therefore
when I heard he had gone off to Paris with five
hundred francs to buy a new crank, I thought the
situation serious.   So, despite the former snub, I
again offered my services.

SHE had her veil up, and, by Jove! she was good
to look upon! The eyes were deep and candid; the
curve of the red lips (a little subdued now) suggested
a delightful sense of humour; her brown hair rippled
over the ears and escaped in curly tendrils on her
white neck.   The girl was delicately balanced, finely
wrought, tempered like a sword-blade.   Something
in my inner workings seemed to cry out with pleasure at her perfections; a very unusual nervousness
got hold of me when I spoke to her.

It ended in my flying off to the Avenue de la
Grande Armée to search for the missing man and
another crank.   You remember my earliest automobile experiences were with a Benz, as so many
people's have been, and I knew where to go.   Nothing had been heard of the man; I bribed a fellow to
take a crank out of another car, and on the way
back a wild idea occurred to me.   I was obliged to
sketch it to the astonished Almond, commanded
him to deadly secrecy, then offered my own services
to the beautiful American girl in place of her former
chauffeur, absconded.   The whole thing came into
my mind in a flash as I was spinning through the
Bois, and I hadn't time to think of the difficulties
in which I might get landed.   I only felt that this
was the prettiest girl I had ever seen, and determined at any price to see a good deal more of her.

Only one way of doing that occurred to me. I couldn't say to her, "I am Mr. John Winston, a perfectly respectable person. I have been seized with a strong and sudden admiration for your beauty. Will you let me go with you on your trip through France?" Even an American girl would have been staggered at that. The situation called for an immediate decision—either I was to lose the girl, or resort to a trick. You quite see how it was, don't you?

In the first instant there came a complication. I had stopped my car a minute in the Bois to scribble a character for my new self—James Brown, from my old self—John Winston; but as soon as I presented this piece of writing to back up my application for the place, Miss Molly Randolph (I may as well give you her name) exclaimed that she knew my mother. Such is life! It seems they met in Paris. But the die was cast, and she engaged me. I trusted the Napier to Almond, giving him general instructions to keep as near to us as he could, without letting himself be seen, and for the last two days I have been *chauffeur*, *mécanicien*, call it what you will. to the most charming girl in this exceedingly satisfactory world.

By this time I know that your eyes are wide open. I can picture you stretched in your *chaise longue* at Davos in the sunshine reading this and whistling softly to yourself. I have no time to write more to-night; the rest must wait.

Your very sincere and excited friend,

JACK WINSTON.

HOTEL DE LONDRES, AMBOISE,
December 3

My dear Montie,

The plot thickens. She is *Superb*. But things are happening which I didn't foresee, and which I don't like. I have to suppress a Worm, and suppressed he shall be. I am writing this letter to you in my bedroom. It is three in the morning, and a lovely night—more like spring than winter. Through my wide-open window the only sound that comes in is the lapping of the lazy Loire against the piers of the great stone bridge. I have not been to bed; I shall not go to bed, for I have something to do when dawn begins. Though I have worked hard to-day, I am not tired; I am too excited for fatigue. But I must give you a sketch of what has happened during the last few days. It is a comfort and a pleasure to me to be able to unburden myself to your sympathetic heart. You will read what I write with patience, I know, and with interest, I hope. That you will often smile, I am sure.

I sent you a line from Orleans, telling you that I had got myself engaged as *chauffeur* to Miss Molly Randolph at Suresnes. Well, the *garage* man and I managed to fit the new crank into my lovely employer's abominable car, and about three or four in the afternoon we were ready to take the road. As

I tucked the rug round the ladies Miss Randolph threw me an appealing look. "My aunt," she said, "declares that it is quite useless to go on, as she is sure we shall never get anywhere. But it *is* a good car, isn't it, Brown, and we *shall* get to Tours, shan't we?" "It's a *great* car, miss," I said quite truthfully and very heartily. "With this car I'd guarantee to take you comfortably all round Europe." Heaven knows that this boast was the child of hope rather than experience; but it would have been too maddening to have the whole thing knocked on the head at the beginning by the fears of a timorous elderly lady. "You hear, Aunt Mary, what Brown says," said the girl, with the air of one who brings an argument to a close, and I hastened to start the car.

By Jove! The compression was strong! I wasn't prepared for it after the simple twist of the hand, which is all that is necessary to start the Napier, and the recoil of the starting-handle nearly broke my wrist. But I got the engine going with the second try, jumped to my place in front of the ladies (you understand that it is a phaeton-seated car), and started very gingerly up the hill. Though I was once accustomed to a belt-driven Benz (you remember my little 3½ horse-power "halfpenny Benz," as I came to call it), that had the ordinary fast and loose pulleys, while this German monstrosity is driven by a jockey-pulley, an appliance fiendishly contrived, as it seemed to me, especially for breaking belts quickly. The car too is steered by a tiller worked with the left hand, and there are so many different levers to manipulate that to drive the thing properly one ought to be a modern Briareus.

I must say, though, that the thing has power. It bumbled in excellent style on the second speed up the long hill of Suresnes; but when we got to the level and changed speeds, I put the jockey on a trifle too quickly, and snick! went the belt. I was awfully anxious that my new mistress shouldn't think me a duffer, that she shouldn't lose confidence in her car and me, and determine to bring her tour to an abrupt end; so as soon as I felt the snap I turned round saying it was only a broken belt that could be mended in no time. She smiled delightfully. "How nice of you to take it so well!" she said. "Rattray seemed to think that when a belt broke the end of the world had come."

Now to mend a belt seems the easiest thing going, and so it is when you merely have to hammer a fastening through it and turn the ends over. But in this car you have to make the joint with coils of twisted wire. Simple as it is to do in a workshop, this belt-mending is a most irritating affair by the roadside, and when done I found by subsequent experiences that the wires wear through and tear out after less than a hundred miles.

On this first day, not having the hang of the job, I found it disgustingly tedious. To begin with, to get at the pulleys I had to open the back of the car, and that meant lifting down all the carefully strapped luggage and depositing it by the roadside. Then the wire and tools were either in a cupboard under the floor of the car or in a box under the ladies' seats, which meant disturbing them every time one wanted anything. How different to my beautifully planned Napier, where every part is easily accessible !

The mending of that third speed-belt took me half an hour, and after that we made some progress; but dusk coming on, I suggested to the ladies that as there was very little fun in travelling in the dark, I thought they had better stay the night at Versailles, going on to Orleans the next day. They agreed.

I had thought out plans for my own comfort. I knew that at some of the smaller country inns there would be no rooms for servants, and that I should have to eat with the ladies, which suited me exactly. In the larger towns, rather than mess with the couriers, valets, and maids, I should simply instal my employers in one hotel, then quietly go off myself to another. That is what I did at Versailles. I saw the ladies into the best hotel in the town, drove the car into the stable-yard, and went out to watch for Almond. He had followed us warily and had stopped the Napier in a side street two hundred yards away. I joined him, and we drove to a quiet hotel about a quarter of a mile from Miss Randolph's. I had my luggage taken in, bathed, changed, and dined like a prince, instructing Almond to be up at six next morning and thoroughly clean and oil the German car, making a lot of new fastenings in spare belts. Later in the day he is to follow us to Orleans with the Napier. Thus I live the double life—by day the leather-clad *chauffeur;* by night the English gentleman travelling on his own car. The plans

seem well laid; I cover my tracks carefully; I don't
see how detection can come.

With a good deal of inward fear and trembling I
drove the car at eight the next morning to the door
of Miss Randolph's hotel. She and her masked and
goggled aunt appeared at once, and in five minutes
the luggage was strapped on behind.

"Now please understand," said the girl, with a
twinkle of merriment, in her eyes, "that this is to be
a pilgrimage, not a meteor flight. Even if this car's
capable of racing, which I guess it isn't, I don't want
to race. I just want to glide; I want to see everything; to drink in impressions every instant."

This suited me exactly, for it gave me a chance
of humouring and studying the uncouth thing that
I was called upon to drive. I had come out to
Versailles to avoid the direct route to Orleans by
Etampes, which is *pavé* nearly all the way, and practically impassable for automobiles. From Versailles
there is a good route by Dourdan and Angerville,
which, if not picturesque, at least passes through
agreeable, richly cultivated country. The road is
exceedingly *accidentée* on leaving Versailles, and I
drove with great care down the dangerous descent
to Châteaufort, and also down the hill at St. Rémy,
which leads to the valley of the Yvette. Till beyond
Dourdan the road is one long switchback, and it is
but fair to record that the solid German car climbed
the hills with a kind of lumbering sturdiness much to
its credit. At Dourdan we lunched, and soon after
entered on the long, level road to Orleans. The car
travelled well—for it, and the day's record of sixty-

seven miles was only three breakages of belts. To
my relief and surprise we actually got to Orleans in
time for dinner. I was a proud man when I drove
my employers into the old-fashioned courtyard of
the d'Orleans. Almond, I knew, was at the St.
Aignan with the Napier, and there I presently joined
him, to hear that he had done the total run from
Versailles, with an hour's stop for lunch, in under the
four hours, the car running splendidly all the way.
Almond does not at all understand why he is left
alone, and why I have gone off to drive two ladies in
an out-of-date German car which any self-respecting
automobilist would be ashamed to be seen on in
France. He looks at me queerly, and would like to
ask questions; but being a good servant as well as a
good mechanic, he doesn't, and kindly puts up with
his master's whims.

My orders were to be ready for the ladies at ten
the next morning, and when punctually to the
moment I drove the car into the courtyard, I found
them waiting for me. Miss Randolph volunteered
the news that she and her aunt had been round the
town in a cab to see the sites connected with the
Maid, but that she had found it very difficult to
picture things as they were, so modernised is the
town.

The morning we left Orleans was exquisite. The
car went well; the magnificent Loire was brimming
from bank to bank, and not meandering among dis-
figuring sand-banks, as it does later in the year; the
wide, green landscape shone through a glitter of
sunshine; and here and there in the blue sky floated

a mass of tumbled white cloud. Our little party at first was silent. I think the beauty of the scene influenced us all, even Aunt Mary; and the thrumming of the motor formed a monotonous undercurrent to our thoughts.

As I've told you, the German horror is phaeton-seated, and for me in front to talk comfortably to any lady behind is not easy. In driving, one can't take one's attention much off the road, so Miss Molly has to lean forward and shout over my shoulder. A curious and delightful kind of understanding is growing up between us. You know that the history of this part of France is fairly familiar to me, and I've already done the castles twice before. What I've forgotten, I've studied up in the evenings, so as to be indispensable to Miss Randolph. At first she spoke to me very little, only a kind word now and then such as one throws to a servant; but I could hear much of what she said to her aunt, and her comments on things in general were sprightly and original. She had evidently read a good deal, looked at things freshly, and brought to bear on the old Court history of France her own quaint point of view. Her enthusiasm was ever ready—bubbling, but never gushing, and I eagerly kept an ear to the windward not to miss the murmur of the geographical and historical fountain behind my back.

"Aunt Mary," on the contrary, has a vague and ordinary mind, being more interested in what she is going to have for luncheon than in what she is going to see. The girl, therefore, is rather thrown back upon herself. I burned to join in the talk, yet I

dared not step out of the character I had assumed.
As it turned out, fortune was waiting to befriend me.

We were bowling along through Meung, when I
suddenly spied on the other side of the river the
square and heavy mass of Notre Dame de Cléry,
and almost without thinking, I pointed it out to
Miss Randolph. "There is Cléry," I said, "where
Louis the Eleventh is buried. You remember, in
Quentin Durward ? The church is worth seeing. It's
almost a pity we didn't go that side of the river."
Then I stopped, rather confused, fearing I had
given myself away. There was a moment's astonished silence, and I was afraid Miss Randolph would
see the back of my neck getting red.

"Why, *Brown!*" she cried, leaning forward over
my shoulder, "you know these things; you've read
history?"

"Oh yes, miss," I said. "I've read a bit here and
there, such books as I could get hold of. I was always interested in history and architecture, and
that sort of thing. Besides," I went on hastily,
"I've travelled this road before with a gentleman
who knows a good deal about this part of France."

I don't think that was disingenuous, was it?—for
I hope I've a right to call myself "a gentleman."

"How lucky for us!" cried Miss Randolph, and
I heard her congratulating herself to her aunt, because they had got hold of a *cicerone* and *chauffeur*
in one. After that she began to talk to me a good
deal, and now she seems to show a kind of wondering interest in testing the amount of my knowledge,
which I take care to clothe in common words and

not to show *too* much. You must admit the situation grows in piquancy.

At Mer we crossed the Loire by the suspension bridge and ran the eight miles to Chambord, meaning to lunch there, and go on to Blois after seeing the Château. It was a grand performance for the car to run nearly three hours without accident. While luncheon was being prepared I filled up the water-tanks (even this simple task involved lifting all the luggage off the car), washed with some invaluable Hudson's soap, which I had brought from my own car, and made myself smart for *déjeuner*. The eating business will, I can see, be one of my chief difficulties. At Chambord, for instance, in the small hotel, there is, of course, no special room for servants. As I have no fondness for eating in stuffy kitchens when it can be avoided, I wandered sedately into the *salle à manger*, where Miss Randolph and her aunt were already seated, and took a place at the further end of the same long table (we were the only people in the room). Aunt Mary looked for an instant a little discomposed at the idea of lunching with her niece's hired mechanic, but Miss Randolph, noticing this—she sees everything—shot me a welcoming smile. Then the paying difficulty is an odious one. Of course, at the end of the meal my bill goes to her, and she pays for me: "*Mécanicien, déjeuner*——" so much. Picture it! Of course, I can't protest, as this is the custom; but I am keeping a strict account of all her expenses on my account, and one day shall square our accounts somehow—I don't at present see how. I have formed the idea that by-and-by I may offer to act also as courier, relieving her of the bother of making payments, and so on. If I can work that, I'll deduct my own lot and pay it myself, the chances being that as she is careless about money she won't notice that I've done so, only thinking, perhaps, that I am a clever chap to run things so cheaply.

There's another thing which gives me the "wombles," as those delightful Miss Bryants used to call the feeling they had when they were looking forward to any event with a mixture of excitement, fear, and embarrassment.

Well, I have the "wombles" when I think of the moment, near at hand, when Miss Randolph will hand me my weekly wage, which I have put at the modest figure of fifty francs a week; but I am getting away from the *déjeuner* at Chambord.

We had just finished the *croûte au pot*, when there came a whirr! outside, upon which Miss Randolph looked questioningly at me. "A little Pieper," I said. "How wonderful!" she exclaimed. "Can you really tell different makes of cars just by their sound?" "Anyone can do that," I informed her, "with practice; you will yourself by the time you get to the end of this journey. Each car has its characteristic note. The De Dion has a kind of screaming whirr; the Benz a pulsing throb; the Panhard a thrumming; a tricycle a noise like a miniature Maxim."

The driver of the Pieper came in. His get-up was the last outrageous word of automobilism—

leather cap with ear-flaps, goggles and mask, a ridiculously shaggy coat of fur, and long boots of skin up to his thighs—a suitable costume for an Arctic explorer, but mighty fantastic in a mild French winter. You know these posing French automobilists. At sight of a beautiful girl, he made haste to take off his hat and goggles, revealing himself as a good-looking fellow with abnormally long eyelashes, which I somehow resented. He preened himself like a bird, twisted up the ends of his black moustache, and prepared for conquest. Catching Miss Randolph's eye, he smiled; she answered with that delightful American frankness which the Italian and the Frenchman misconstrue, and in a moment they were talking motor-car as hard as they could go. The poor *chauffeur* was ignored.

It undermines one's sense of self-importance to find how quickly one can be unclassed. I tasted at this moment the mortification of service. Once in an hotel at Biarritz I gave to the *valet de chambre* a hat and a couple of coats that I didn't want any more. They were in good condition, and he was overwhelmed with the value of the gift. "Monsieur is too kind," the fellow said; "such clothes are too good for me. They are all right for you, but for *nous autres !*"—the "others," who neither expect the good things of life nor envy those who have them. The expression implies the belief that the world is divided into two parts—the ones and the other ones.

Now, as I heard my sweet and clever little lady babbling automobilism with all the wisdom of an amateur of six weeks, I felt that I was indeed one of the Others. Though the Frenchman was to me a manifest Worm (in that he was supercilious, puffed up with conceit, taking it for granted that women should fall down and worship him) and a ridiculous braggart, I had to see her receive his open admiration with equanimity and listen to his stories with credulity, *my* business being to eat in silence and "thank Heaven" (though not "fasting") that I was allowed in the presence of my betters. Still, I would have gone through more than that to be near her, to hear her talk, and see her smile, for frankly this girl begins to interest me as no other woman has.

"Ah, how I have travelled to-day!" the Frenchman said, throwing his hands wide apart. "I left Paris this morning, to-morrow I shall be in Biarritz. To-day I have killed a dog and three hens. On the front of my car just now I found the bones and feathers of some birds, which miscalculated their distance and could not get away in time." Miss Randolph gave a little cry, translating for her aunt, who has no French.

"Shocking!" ejaculated Aunt Mary. "A regular juggernaut."

"Your car does not go as fast as that, mademoiselle?" the Frenchman went on. "A little heavy, I should think; a slow hill-climber?"

"On the contrary," Miss Randolph fired up. "Though my car has—er—*some* drawbacks, it goes splendidly uphill, doesn't it, Brown?"

"That is its strong point," I answered, grateful for the unexpected and kindly word of recognition thrown to me, one of the Others; but the Frenchman did not deign to notice the *chauffeur*.

"Capital!" cried he. "If mademoiselle be willing, and a hill can be found in the neighbourhood, I should like to wager my Pieper against her seven-horse-power German car. I had an odd experience the other day," he went on. "My motor stopped for want of *essence;* luckily it was in a village, but there wasn't a drop of *essence* to be bought—all the shops were sold out. What do you think I did, mademoiselle? I filled the tank with absinthe from a *café*, and got home on that. Not many would have thought of it, eh?"

"Few indeed," said I to myself, for it was news to me that his carburetter could burn heavy oil. While I was reflecting that automobiling, like fishing, is a pursuit whose followers are peculiarly ready to sacrifice truth on the altar of picturesqueness, luncheon was over, and we all rose. With what seemed to me detestable impertinence, though clearly not understood as such by innocent Miss Randolph, the Frenchman sauntered by the side of the ladies as if to go with them to the Château. Perhaps my young mistress was touched by the look of gloom that doubtless clouded my insignificant features, for she promptly and cordially tendered me an invitation to go with them. "You know, Brown," she said, "we look on you as our guide as well as our *chauffeur*" ("and I must be your watch-dog too, though it isn't in the contract," I grumbled to myself, "if you are going to allow every automobilist who claims the right of fellowship to thrust himself upon you").

Even Aunt Mary was impressed as we passed into
the inner court of Chambord, and Miss Randolph
(whose sympathy and imagination throws her at
once into harmony with her surroundings) drew a
quick breath of half-awed astonishment at sight of
this enormous structure, more like a city than
a single house, with its prodigious towers, its extraordinary assemblage of pinnacles, gables, turrets,
cones, chimneys and gargoyles. The Frenchman
minced along at her side, twirling his moustache,
and making great play with those long-lashed eyes
of his. I divined his intention to outdistance us,
and get Miss Randolph to himself in the labyrinth
of vast, empty rooms through which our party was
paraded by a languid guide; but thwarted him by
hastening Aunt Mary's steps and keeping upon their
heels in my new character of watch-dog. I was
more annoyed than I care to tell you when I saw
that she seemed to like his idiotic compliments; but
when I heard him tell her airily that Chambord was
built by Louis the Fourteenth, and Miss Randolph
turned questioningly to me with a puzzled little
wrinkle on her forehead, I felt that my time had
come.

I began something reprehensively like a lecture on
Chambord, putting myself by Miss Randolph's side,
and determined that the Frenchman should get no
further chance. I pointed out the constant recurrence
of the salamander, the emblem of Francis the First,
the builder of the house, and I told how he had
selected this sandy waste to build it on, because the
Comtesse de Thoury had once lived near by, she

having been one of the earliest loves of that oft-loving King. I enlarged upon the characteristics of French Renaissance architecture, pointed out the unity in variety of the design of Pierre Nepveu, the obscure but splendid genius who planned the house as something between a fortified castle and an Italian palace; showed them the H entwined with a crescent on those parts of the house that were built by Henry the Second; and sketched the history of the place, talking about Marshal Saxe, Stanislas of Poland, the Revolution of 1792, and the subsequent tenancy of Berthier. I can tell you that when once I was started, the absinthe-driver was bowled over. I simply sprawled all over Chambord, talked for once as well as I knew how, directed all my remarks to Miss Randolph, who— "though I say it as shouldn't"—seemed dazzled by my fireworks. An English girl must have been struck with the incongruity of a hired mechanic spouting French history like a public lecturer, but she, I think, only put it down to some difference in the standard of English education. Anyhow, the Frenchman was done for, and Miss Randolph and I plunged into an interesting talk, shunting the new acquaintance upon Aunt Mary. As she can speak no French and he no English, they must have had a "Jack-Sprat-and-his-wife" experience.

For that happy hour while we wandered through the echoing-rooms of Chambord, climbed the wonderful double staircase, and walked about the intricate roof, I was no longer James Brown, the hired mechanic, but John Winston, private gentleman and

man at large, with a taste for travel. There came
a horrid wrench when I had to remember that I had
chosen to make myself one of the unclassed, one
of the "others." The autumnal twilight was falling;
we had to get to Blois on a car that might commit
any atrocity at any instant. Yet, strange to say,
it had a magnanimous impulse, started easily, and
ran smoothly. The somewhat subdued Frenchman
started just before us on his little Pieper, and soon
outpaced our solid chariot. We went back to St.
Dié, took the road by the Loire, and as dusk was
falling crossed the camel-backed bridge over the
great river, and went up the Rue Denis Pépin into
the ancient city of Blois. The Château does not
show its best face to the riverside, being hemmed in
by other buildings, so I drove past our hotel and on
to the pretty green *place* where the great many-
windowed Château springs aloft from its huge foun-
dation. "The famous Château of Blois," I remarked,
waving a hand towards it. "The old home of the
kings of France." We all sat and looked up at the
huge, silent building, the glowing colours of its
recessed windows catching the last beams of departing day.

"I suppose its only tenants now are ghosts," said
Miss Randolph. "I can imagine that I see wicked
Catherine de Medicis glaring at us from that high
window near the tower." It was an impressive intro-
duction to one of the greatest monuments of France,
and after we had gazed a little longer I turned the
car and drove back into the courtyard of the Grand
Hotel de Blois, where tame partridges pecked at

grain upon the ground, many dogs gambolled, and foreign birds bickered and chattered in huge cages. At the entrance was the Frenchman, all eyes and eyelashes, darting forward to help Miss Randolph from her car.

I grew weary to nausea of this shallow, pretentious ass, with no knowledge of his own land. It began to shape itself in my mind that though a gentleman in exterior he was the common or garden fortune-hunter, or perhaps worse. Finding a beautiful American girl travelling *en automobile*, chaperoned only by a rather foolish and pliable aunt, he fancied her an easy prey to his elaborate manners and eye-lashes. Knowing we were coming to the "Grand," I had directed Almond to drive the Napier to the "France," and my duty for the day being over, I was about to go across to change and dine, when I saw Miss Randolph in the hall. She was annoyed, she told me, to find that the best suite of rooms were taken by some rich Englishman and his daughter, and she had to put up with second-rate ones. "Poor Monsieur Talleyrand," she ended, "has little more than a cupboard to sleep in." Talleyrand, then, was the name of the Frenchman. "Oh, is he stopping here?" I asked. "He said he was going on at once to Biarritz."

"He's changed his mind," said she. "He's so impressed with Chambord that he says it's a pity not to see all the other châteaux, which are so impor-tant in the history of his own country. He asked Aunt Mary if we should mind his going at the same time with us. So *of course* she said we wouldn't."

All this, if you please, with the most candid air of guilelessness, which I actually believe was genuine.

"She said *what?*" I demanded, quite forgetting my part in my rage.

"She said," repeated Miss Randolph slowly and with dignity, "that we would not mind his seeing the châteaux when we see them. Why should we mind? The poor young man won't do us any harm, and it's quite right of him to want to see his own castles, because, anyhow, they're a great deal more his than ours."

I was still out of myself, or rather out of Brown.

"But is it possible, my dear Miss Randolph," I was mad enough to exclaim (I, who had never before risen above the level of a humble "miss"), "that you and Miss Kedison believe in that flimsy excuse? The castles——"

"Yes, the *castles*," she repeated, very properly taking the word out of my mouth; and the worst of it was that she was completely right in setting me in my place, setting me down hard. "I am surprised at you, Brown. You are a splendid mechanic, and—and you have travelled and read such a lot that you are a very good guide too, and because I think we're lucky to have got you I treat you quite differently from an ordinary *chauffeur*." (If you could have heard that "ordinary" as she said it! There was hope in it in the midst of humiliation; but I dared not let a gleam dart from my respectful eye.) "Still, you must remember, please, that you are engaged for certain things and not for others. If I need a protector besides Aunt Mary, I may tell you."

I could have burst into unholy laughter to hear the poor child; but I bottled it up, and only ventured to say, with a kind of soapy meekness which I hoped might lather over the real presumption," I beg your pardon, miss, and I hope you won't be offended; but, as you say, I have travelled a little, and I know something of Frenchmen. They don't always understand American young ladies as well as——"

"'As well as Englishmen,' I suppose you were going to say," snapped she, that dimpled chin of hers suddenly seeming to assume a national squareness I'd never observed. "But Monsieur Talleyrand, though a Frenchman, is a gentleman."

That's what I had to swallow, my boy. The inference was that a French gentleman was, at worst, a cut above an English mechanic, and with that she turned her back on me and ran upstairs with such a rustling of unseen silk things as made me feel her very petticoats were bristling with indignation.

I could have shaken the girl. And the things I said to myself as I stalked over to my own hotel won't bear repeating; they might set the mail-bag on fire; combustibles aren't allowed in the post, I believe. I swore that (among other things) one such snubbing was enough. If Miss Randolph wanted to get herself in the devil of a scrape, she could do it, but I wasn't going to stand by and look complacently on while that smirking Beast made fools of her and her aunt. I'd clear out to-morrow; didn't care a hang whether she found out the trick I'd played or not.

That mood lasted about ten minutes, then I began

to realise that, talking of beasts, there was something of the sort inside my own leather coat, and that if anyone deserved a shaking, it was Jack Winston, and not that poor, pretty little thing. I was bound to stop on in the place and protect her, whether she knew she wanted any protection except Aunt Mary's (oh, Lord!) or not. Besides, I wanted the place, since it was the best I could expect for the present, and where Talleyrand (?) was, there would I be also, so long as he was near Her.

Bath and dinner brought me once more as near to an angelic disposition as I hope to attain in this sphere; and, while I was supposed to be earning my screw by cleaning the loathsome car, and making new fastenings for spare belts, I was complacently watching poor Almond in the throes of these Herculean labours. N.B.—It's only fair to myself to tell you that Almond is getting double wages, and is quite satisfied, though I'm persuaded he thinks he has a madman for a master.

About half-past nine next morning (that's yesterday, in case you're getting mixed) I was hanging round the German chariot with a duster, pretending to flick specks off it, though Almond had left none, when Miss Randolph, Aunt Mary, and the alleged Talleyrand came out of the coffee-room, laughing and talking like the best of friends. Talleyrand was now in ordinary clothes, perhaps to point the difference between himself and a mere professional *chauffeur*. Miss Randolph looked adorable. She'd put off her motoring get-up, and was no end of a swell. This I saw without seeming to see, for we

.ad not met since our scene. I didn't know where
I stood with her, but thought it prudent meanwhile
to wear a humble air of conscious rectitude, misunderstood.

Talleyrand was swaggering along without a glance
at the *chauffeur* (why not, indeed ?) when Miss
Randolph hung back, looked round, and then
stopped. "Oh, Brown, do you know as much about
the Chateau of Blois as you did about Chambord?"
asked she, in a voice as sweet as the Lost Chord.

"Yes, miss, I think I do," said I, lifting my black
leather cap.

"Then, are you too busy to come with us ? "

"No, miss, not at all, if I can be of any service."

"But, you know, you needn't come unless you
like. Maybe it bores you to be a guide."

Now, if I'd been a gentleman and not a *chauffeur*,
perhaps I should have had a right to suspect just
a morsel of innocent, kittenish coquetry in this. As
it is with me—and with her—if there's anything of
the sort, it's wholly unconscious. But it's the most
adorable type of girl who flirts a little with everything human—man, woman, or child—and doesn't
know it. I take no flattering unction to myself as
Brown. Nevertheless I dutifully responded that it
gave me pleasure to make use of such small knowledge as I possessed, and was grateful to her for
not hearing Talleyrand murmur that he'd provided
himself with the *Guide Joanne*. After that I could
afford to be moderately complacent, even though
I had to walk in the rear of the party, and no one
took notice of me until I was wanted.

That time came, when we'd wound round the path under the commanding old Château, with its long lines of windows, and reached the exquisite Gothic doorway. From that moment it was the Chambord business over again; and I thanked my foresight for having stopped out of my bed half the night, fagging up all the historical details I'd forgotten. These I brought out with a naturalistic air of having been brought up on them since earliest infancy.

Miss Randolph chatters pretty American French, but doesn't understand as much as she speaks when it's reeled off by the yard, so to say; therefore my explanations in English were more profitable than the French of the official guide, who fell into the background. My delightful American maiden has never travelled abroad before, and she brings with her a fresh eagerness for all the old things that are so new to her. It is a constant joy even for poor handicapped Brown to go about with her, finding how invariably she seizes on the right thing, which she knows by instinct rather than cultivation—though she's evidently what she would call a "college girl."

I halted my little party before the Louis the Twelfth gateway, made them admire the equestrian statue of the good King, drew their attention to the beautiful chimneys and the adornments of the roof, with the agreeable porcupine of Louis, the mild ermine and the constantly recurring festooned rope of that important lady, Anne of Brittany. Then I led them inside, rejoicing in Talleyrand's air of resentful remoteness from my guidance. I scored, too, in his superficial knowledge of English. In the midst of my ciceronage, however, I thought of you, and how we had discussed plans of this trip together. You had looked forward particularly to the Château; and as you've urged me to paint for you what you can't see (this time), your blood be on your own head if I bore you.

You would be happy in the courtyard of the Château, for it would be to your mind, as to mine, one of the most delightful things in Europe. It's a sort of object lesson in French architecture and history, showing at least three periods; and when Miss Randolph looked up at that perfect, open staircase, bewildering in its carved, fantastic beauty, I wasn't surprised to have her ask if she were dreaming it, or if we saw it too. "It's lace, stone lace," she said. And so it is. She coined new adjectives for the windows, the sculptured cornices, the exquisite and ingenious perfection of the incomparable façade.

"I could be so *good* if I always had this staircase to look at!" she exclaimed. "It didn't seem to have any effect on Catherine de Medici's soul; but then I suppose when she lived here she stopped indoors most of the time, making up poisons. I'm sorry I said yesterday that Francis the First had a ridiculous nose. A man who could build this had a right to *have* anything he liked, or *do* anything he liked."

And you should have seen her stare when Talleyrand bestowed an enthusiastic *"Comme c'est beau!"* on the left wing of the courtyard, for which Gaston d'Orleans' bad taste and foolish extravagance is responsible—a thing not to be named with the joyous Renaissance façade of Francis.

When Miss Randolph could be torn away, we went inside, and throwing off self-consciousness in the good cause, I flung myself into the drama of the Guise murder. Little did I know what I was letting myself in for. My one desire was to interest Miss Randolph, and (incidentally, perhaps) show her what a clever chap she had got for a *chaffeur*— though he *wasn't* a gentleman, and Talleyrand was.

I pointed from a window to the spot where stands the house from which the Duc de Guise was decoyed from the arms of his mistress; showed where he stood impatiently leaning against the tall mantelpiece, waiting his audience with Henri the Third; pointed to the threshold of the *Vieux Cabinet* where he was stabbed in the back as he lifted the arras; told how he ran, crying *"a moi!"* and where he fell at last to die, bleeding from more than forty wounds, given by the Forty Gentlemen of the Plot; showed the little oratory in which, while the murderous work went on, two monks gabbled prayers for its successful issue.

I got quite interested in my own harangue, inspired by those stars Miss Randolph has for eyes, and didn't notice that my audience had increased, until, at this point, I suddenly heard a shocked echo of Aunt Mary's "Oh!" of horror, murmured in a strange voice, close to my shoulder. Then I looked round and saw a man and a girl, who were evidently hanging on my words.

The man was the type one sees on advertisements

of succulent sauces; you know, the smiling, full-
bodied, red-faced, good-natured John Bull sort, who
is depicted smacking his lips over a meal accompanied by The Sauce, which has produced the
ecstasy. One glance at his shaven upper lip, his
chin beard, and his keen but kindly eye, and I set
him down as a comfortable manufacturer on a holi-
day—a Lancashire or Yorkshire man. The girl
might be a daughter or young wife; I thought the
former. A handsome creature, with big black eyes
and a luscious, peach-like colour; style of hairdressing
conscientiously copied from Queen Alexandra's; fine
figure, well shown off by a too elaborate dress probably bought at the wrong shop in Paris; you felt
she had been sent by doting parents to a boarding-
school for "the daughters of noblemen and gentlemen"; no expense spared.

It was she who had echoed Aunt Mary; and when
I turned she bridled. Yes, I think that's the only
word for what she did. But it was the man who
spoke.

"I beg your pardon," he said, dividing the apology
among the whole party, and taking off his unspeak-
ably solid hat to the ladies. "I hope there's no
objection to me and my daughter listening to this
very intelligent guide? She's learned French, but
it doesn't seem to work here; she thinks it's too
Parisian for Blois, but anyhow, we couldn't either of
us understand a word the French guide said, so we
took the liberty of joining on to you, with a great
deal of pleasure and profit."

He had a sort of engaging ingenuousness, mixed

with shrewdness of the provincial order, and I could see that he appealed to my American girl, though I don't think she cottoned to the daughter. She smiled at the papa, as if for the sake of her own; and in a few pretty words practically made him a present of me, that is, she offered to let him share me for the rest of the tour round the Château. I was not sorry, as I hoped that the daughter might occupy the attention of Monsieur Talleyrand; and as, under these new conditions, we continued our explorations, I adroitly contrived to divide off the party as follows: Miss Randolph, the Lancashire man (his accent had placed him in my mind), and myself; Aunt Mary, the new girl, and our gentleman of the eyelashes. This arrangement was satisfactory to me and the old man, whether it was to anybody else or not; and so grouped, we went through the apartments of Catherine de Medicis (Aunt Mary pronounced "those little poison cupboards of hers *vurry* cunning; *so* cute of her to keep changing them around all the time!"), and out on the splendid balconies.

The Lancashire man, thanks to Miss Randolph's permission, made himself quite at home with me, bombarding me with historical questions. But it was evident that he was puzzled as to my status.

"You are a first-rate lecturer," said he. "I suppose that's your profession?"

"Not entirely," said I, with a glance at Miss Randolph; but she was enjoying the joke, and not minded to enlighten him. Probably he supposed that leather jacket and leggings was the regulation costume of a lecturing guide.

"Do you engage by the day," he inquired, "or by the tour?"

"So far, I have engaged by the tour, sir," I returned, playing up for the amusement of my lady.

He scratched his chin reflectively. "Baedeker recommends several of these old castles in this part of the country," said he. "Do you know 'em all?"

I answered that I had visited them.

"All as interesting as this?"

"Quite, in different ways."

"Hm! Do you speak French?"

"Fairly," I modestly responded.

"Well, if this young lady hasn't engaged you for too long ahead, I should like to talk to you about going on with us. I didn't think I should care to have a courier, but a chap like you would add a good deal to the pleasure of a trip. Seems to me you are a sort of walking encyclopædia. I would pay you whatever you asked, in reason——"

"And, oh, papa, he might go on with us all the way to Cannes!" chipped in the daughter, which was my first intimation that she was listening. But she had joined the forward group, and the words addressed to Pa were apparently spoken at me. I dared not look at Miss Randolph, but I hoped that a background of other people's approval might set me off well in her eyes.

I was collecting my wits for an adequate answer, when she relieved me of the responsibility. I might even say she snapped up the young lady from Lancashire.

"I'm afraid I must disappoint you," she replied for

her *chauffeur*. "He is engaged to *me*. I mean" (and she blushed divinely) "he is under engagement to remain with my aunt and myself for some time We are making a tour on an automobile."

"I beg your pardon, I'm sure," said the old fellow, as the American and the English girl eyed each other—or each other's dresses. "I didn't understand the arrangement. When you *are* free, though," he went on, turning to me, "you might just let me know. We're thinking of travelling about for some time, and I've taken a liking to your ways. I'm at the 'Grand' here at Blois for the day, then we go on to Tours, and so by easy stages to the Riviera. At Cannes, we shall settle down for a bit, as my daughter has a friend who's expecting us to meet her there. But I'll give you my card, with my home address on it, and a letter, or, better still, a wire, would be forwarded." He then thanked Miss Randolph for me, thanked me for myself, and, with a last flourish of trumpets, handed me his card.

By this time we had "done" the castle, as conscientious Aunt Mary would say, and were parting. All exchanged bows (Miss Randolph's and the Lancashire girl's expressive of armed neutrality) and parted. I thereupon glanced at the card and got a sensation.

"Mr. Jabez Barrow, Edenholme Hall, Liverpool," was what I read. That conveys little to you, though as an address it has suggestive charm, but to me it meant nothing less than a complication. Queer, what a little place the world is! To make clear the situation I need only say, "The Cotton King." Yes,

that's it; you've guessed it. These Barrows are my
mother's newest protégés. Jabez Barrow is the
"quaint, original old man" she is so anxious for
me to meet, and, indeed, has made arrangements that
I *should* meet. Miss Barrow is the "beautiful girl
with wonderful eyes and such charming ways," who,
in my dear mother's opinion, would be so desirable
as a daughter-in-law. Had not your doctors knocked
our plans on the head you would have had the
pleasure of being introduced in my company to
the heiress, when I should have made you a present
of my chance to add to your own. As it is—well,
I don't quite see that any bother can come out
of this coincidence, but I must keep a sharp look-
out for myself. I saw no Kodak in the hands of
the gilded ones, or—by-and-by—my mother might
receive a shock. But perhaps they may have possessed and concealed it.

Into the midst of my broodings over the card
broke the voice of Miss Randolph, in whose wake
I was now following down the picturesque old street
to the hotel. Talleyrand was in attendance again,
and she had merely to say that the car was to be ready
for start to Amboise after luncheon. Accordingly I
stepped over to my own private lair, told Almond to
get off at once with my Napier to Amboise, putting
up at a hotel I named and awaiting instructions.

Have you begun to think there's to be no end to
this letter? Well, I shall try to whet your curiosity
for what's still to come by saying that I have availed
myself of a strange blank interval in the middle of
the night for the writing of it, and that dawn can't

now be far off. When it breaks this adventure of mine will have reached a crisis—a distinctly new development. But enough of hints.

This country of the Loire is exquisite; it has both grandeur and simple beauty, and the road winding above the river is practically level and in splendid condition; ideal for motors and "hay-motors." The distance between the good town of Blois and Amboise is less than twenty miles. Any decent-minded motor would whistle along from the great grey Chateau to the brilliant cream-white one under the hour, but that isn't the way of our Demon.

Miss Randolph once said that owning a motor-car was like having a half-tamed dragon in the family. She is quite right about *her* motor-car, poor child! The Demon had been behaving somewhat less fiendishly of late, and I had hopes of a successful run to Amboise, which I particularly desired, as Eyelashes was to accompany us with his Pieper. But this good conduct had been no more than a trick.

The luggage was loaded up; Talleyrand was making himself officious about helping the ladies, who were in the courtyard ready to mount, when the motor took it into its vile head not to start— a little attack of faintness, owing to the petrol being cold perhaps. Of course, there was the usual crowd of hotel servants and loafers to see us off, and beyond, standing as interested spectators on the steps, who but Jabez Barrow and his handsome daughter.

I tell you the perspiration decorated my forehead

in beads when I'd made a dozen fruitless efforts to start that family dragon, Eyelashes maddening me the while with a series of idiotic suggestions. Even Miss Randolph began to get a little nervous, and called out to me, "What *can* be the matter, Brown? I thought you were such a *strong* man too. Do let Monsieur Talleyrand try, as he's an expert."

I could see Eyelashes didn't like that suggestion a little bit, consequently I welcomed it. It's very well to dance about and give advice, quite another thing to do the work yourself; but I gleefully stood aside while he grasped the starting-handle. It takes both strength and knack to start that car, and he had neither. At first he couldn't get the handle round against the compression; then, exerting himself further, there came a terrific back-fire—the handle flew round, knocked him off his feet, and sent him staggering, very pale, into the arms of a white-aproned waiter. I couldn't help grinning, and I fancy Miss Randolph hid a smile behind her handkerchief.

Eyelashes was furious. "It is a horror, that German machine!" he cried. "Such a thing has no right to exist. Look at mine!" He darted to his Pieper, gave one twist of the handle, and the motor instantly leaped into life. Everyone murmured approval at this demonstration of the superiority of France, or rather, Belgium, to Germany; but next moment I had got our motor to start. The ladies dubiously took their places, and under the critical dark eyes of Miss Barrow I steered out into the streets of Blois.

I will spare you the detailed horrors of the next few hours. It seemed to me that to keep that car going one must have the agility of a monkey, the strength of a Sandow, and the resourcefulness of a Sherlock Holmes. Almost everything went wrong that could go wrong. Both chains snapped—that was trifling except for the waste of time, but finally the exhaust-valve spring broke. It was getting dusk by this time, and to replace that spring was one of the grisliest of my automobile experiences. To get at it I had to lift off all the upper body of the car and take out both the inlet and the exhaust valves. As darkness came on, Miss Randolph (who took it all splendidly and laughed at our misfortunes) held a lamp while I wrestled with the spring and valves. The Frenchman, who had kept close to us on his irritatingly perfect little Pieper, I simply used as a labourer, ordering him about as I pleased—my one satisfaction. After an hour's work (much of the time on my back under the car, with green oil dripping into my hair!) I got the new spring on, and we could start again. Then—horror on horror's head!—we had not gone two miles before I heard a strange clack! clack! and looking behind, saw that one of the back tyres was loose, hanging to the wheel in a kind of festoon, like a fat worm.

It was eight o'clock; we had lunched at one; the night was dark; we were still miles short of Amboise; if the tyre came right off, it would be awkward to run on the rim. I explained this, suggesting that we should leave the car for a night at a farmhouse, which presumably existed behind a high, glimmering

white wall near which we happened to halt, and try
to get a conveyance of some sort to drive on to
Amboise.

But I had calculated without Eyelashes. Instantly
he saw his chance, and seized it. Figuratively he
laid his Pieper at the ladies' feet. To be sure, it was
built for only two, but the seat was very wide; there
was plenty or room; he would be only too glad to
whirl them off to the most comfortable hotel at
Amboise, which could be reached in no time. As
for the *chauffeur*, he could be left to look after the car.

The *chauffeur*, however, did not see this in the
same light. Not that he minded the slight hardship,
if any, but to see his liege lady whisked off from
under his eyes by the villain of the piece was too
much.

Think how you would have felt in my place. But
the hideous part was that, like "A" in a "Vanity
Fair" Hard Case, I could do nothing. The proposal
was vexatiously sensible, and I had to stand swallow-
ing my objections while Miss Randolph and her aunt
decided.

I saw her move a step or two towards the Pieper
silently, rather gloomily, but Aunt Mary was grimly
alert. Eyelashes had, I had learned through snatches
of conversation on board the car   een tactful enough
to present Aunt Mary with a little brooch and a
couple of hat-pins of the charming *faïence* made by a
famous man in Blois. Intrinsically of no great value,
they rejoiced in ermine and porcupine crests, with
exquisitely coloured backgrounds, and the guileless
lady's heart had been completely won. She now

emphatically voted for the Frenchman and his car. But I have already noted a little peculiarity of Miss Randolph's, which I have also observed in other delightful girls, though none as delightful as she. If she is undecided about a thing, and somebody else takes it for granted she is going to do it, she is immediately certain that she never contemplated anything of the kind.

This welcome idiosyncrasy now proved my friend. "Why, Aunt Mary," she exclaimed, "you wouldn't have me go off and desert my own car, *in the middle of the night* too? I couldn't think of such a thing. *You* can go with Monsieur Talleyrand, if you want to, but I shall stay here till everything is settled."

I was really sorry for Aunt Mary. She was almost ready to cry.

"You know perfectly well I shouldn't dream of leaving you here, perhaps to be murdered," whimpered she. "Where you stay, I stay."

She had the air of an elderly female Casabianca.

As for Miss Randolph, I adored her when she bade me go with her to investigate what lay behind the wall, and told Talleyrand off for sentinel duty over Aunt Mary and the car in the road.

At first sight the wall seemed a blank one, but I found a large gate, pushed it open, and we walked into the darkness of a great farmyard. Not a glimmer showed the position of the house, but a clatter of hoofs and a chink of light guided us towards a stable, where a giant man with aquiline face was rubbing down a rusty and aged horse. He started and fixed a suspicious stare on me, and I

daresay that I was a forbidding figure in my dirty
leather clothes, with smears of oil upon my face.
His expression lightened a little at sight of my
companion, but he was inflexible in his refusal to
drive us anywhere. His old mare had cast a shoe on
her way home just now; he would not take her out
again. Could he, then, Miss Randolph asked, give
us rooms for the night, and food? As to that he was
not sure, but would consult his wife. He tramped
before us to the big dark house, put down his lantern in the hall, opened a door, and ushered us into
a dark room, following and closing the door behind
him. The room was airless and heavy with the
odour of cooking. The darkness was intense, and
from the midst of it came a strange sound of jabber-
ing and bleating which for the life of me I couldn't
understand. I felt Miss Randolph draw near me as
if for protection, then with the scratch of a match
and a flicker from a lamp which the farmer was
lighting, was revealed the cause of the weird sounds.
Seated by the stove was a pathetically old woman,
with pendulous chin and rheumy eyes. Swinging
her palsied head from side to side, she jabbered and
bleated incoherently to herself, being abandoned to
this plague of darkness doubtless from motives of
economy.

The farmer's wife appeared, and after much discussion it was arranged that the ladies could have
a double-bedded room, and there was a small one
that would do for Monsieur Talleyrand; but the
mécanicien would have to sleep in the barn, where he
could have some clean straw. Supper could be ready

in half an hour, but we were not to expect the luxuries of a hotel.

The farmer and I carried the ladies' hand-luggage upstairs into a mysterious dim region, where all was clean and cold. I had a flickering, candle-lit vision of a big white room, with an enormously high bedstead, bare floor, a rug or two, a chair or two, a shrine, and a washhand-stand with a knitted cover, one basin the size of a porridge-bowl containing a thing like a milk-jug. Then I set down my burden and departed to wheel the great helpless car into the farmyard, and wash my hands with Hudson's soap in a trough under a pump outside the kitchen.

Meanwhile preparations for supper went on, and as I was hungrily hoping for scraps when my betters should have finished, who should pop out but that Angel to say that supper was ready, and would I eat with them! I had been working *so* hard and must be starved. If she had guessed how I longed to kiss her she would have run away indoors much faster than she did.

There was soup, chicken, an omelette, and cheese. Trust a Frenchwoman—even the humblest—to turn out an excellent meal on the shortest notice. Miss Randolph smiled and beamed on them, so that in five minutes the farmer and his wife were her willing slaves. She was delighted with the "adventure," as she called it, declaring that the whole thing would be the greatest fun in the world. She was glad that the horrid tyre had come off, as it gave her the chance, which she would never have had otherwise, of studying French peasant life at first hand. Aunt Mary was called in from outside and acquiesced, as she always did, in the arrangements made by her impetuous niece; the farmer and I had pushed the German car inside the gate and left it; but Talleyrand was fussy about getting proper cover for his smart Pieper, and was not satisfied until he had housed it in a dry barn near the house.

After supper I strolled out into the night, trying, with a pipe between my lips, to think out the details of an alluring new plan which had flashed into my mind.

"Flashed" there, do I say? Forced, rammed in, and pounded down expresses it better. Will you believe it, during supper, that fellow—Eyelashes, I mean—had had **the** audacity to urge upon Miss Randolph that she must now continue the tour on his car!

I was smoking and fuming in the dark, in a corner down by the gateway, when I heard a whisper of silk (I suppose it's linings; I'd know it at the North Pole as hers, now), and detected a shadow which I knew meant Miss Randolph. She came nearer. I saw her distinctly now, for she was carrying a lantern. At first I thought she was looking for me, but she wasn't. She went straight to the car and stood glowering at it for a minute, having set down the lantern. Then she took Something out of the folds of her dress and seemed to feel it with her hand. "Oh, you won't go, won't you?" she inquired sardonically. "You like to break your belts and go dropping your chains about, just to give Brown all the trouble you can, don't you, and keep us from getting anywhere? You think it's enough to be beautiful, and you can be as much of a beast as you like. But you're *not* beautiful. You're horrid, and I hate you! Take that!"

Up went the Something in her hand; it glittered in the yellow light of the lantern. If you will believe it, the girl had got a hatchet and was *chopping at the car*. Her poor vicious little stroke did no great damage, but she chipped off a big flake of varnish and left a white gash.

"Oh!" she exclaimed, as if it had hurt her and not her great lumbering dragon. "Oh, you deserve it, you know, and a lot more. But—but——" and she gave a little gurgling sigh.

I had been on the point of bursting out with uncontrollable laughter, but suddenly I ceased to find the thing funny. I couldn't lurk in ambush and hear any more; I couldn't sneak away—even to spare her feelings—and leave her there to cry, for I felt she was going to cry. So I came out into the circle of lantern-light, shaking the tobacco from my pipe.

"Why, Brown, is that you?" she quavered. "I— I didn't want anyone to see me, and I wasn't crying about the car, but just *Because*—because of everything. I found that hatchet, and—I couldn't help it. I'm sorry now, though. It was mean of me to hit a thing when it's down, even if it is a Beast. It does deserve to be *killed*, though. It's simply no use trying to go on with such a thing—is it?"

Because of the Plan in my mind I replied gloomily that the prospect was rather discouraging.

"Discouraging ! It's impossible !" she cried. "I've been hoping against hope, but I see that now. I *won't* ask poppa to buy me another; it's too ridiculous. So there's nothing left except to go on by train everywhere, unless—you heard how kind Monsieur Talleyrand was about offering to take us on his car."

In the lantern light I thought I saw that she was beginning to look enigmatic, but I couldn't trust my eyes at this moment. There were a good many stars floating before them—not heavenly—the kind I should have liked to make Talleyrand see.

"Yes, miss, I heard," I said brutally, "and, of course, if you and your aunt would like that, I could wire to Mr. Barrow, the gentleman who went round the Château with us to-day, that I was free to take an engagement with him and his daughter."

She turned on me like a flash. "Oh, is *that* what you are thinking of? Well—certainly you may consider yourself free—*perfectly* free. You are under no contract. Go! go to-morrow—or even to-night if you wish. Leave me here with my car. I can go back to Paris, or—or somewhere."

"But I thought you were going on with the French gentleman?" I said.

"I should not think of going with him," she announced icily.

"You said——"

"I said he *invited* me. I never said I meant to go; I couldn't have said it. For I should *hate* going with him. There would be no fun in that at all. I want my own car or none. But that need not matter to you. Go with your Barrows."

"Begging your pardon, miss, I don't want to go with any Barrows."

"But you said——"

"If you wished to get rid of me——"

"*I* wish 'to get rid of' you! I don't repudiate my—business arrangements in that way."

"May I stop on with you, then, miss?" I pleaded at my meekest. "I'll try and do the best I can about the car."

"Oh, do you *really* think there's any hope?" She clasped her hands and looked at me as if I were an oracle. Her eyelashes are very long. I wonder why they are so charming on her and so abominable on a Frenchman?

"I've got an idea in my mind, miss," said I, "that might make everything all right."

"Brown," said she, "you are a kind of leather angel."

Then we both laughed. And I am afraid it occurred to her that the ground we were touching was not calculated to bear a lady and her *mécanicien*, for she turned and ran away

It was not yet ten o'clock, and I had something better to do than crawl into the bed of straw that had been offered me. It was not much more than ten miles to Amboise, and opening the great gate as quietly as I could, I stepped out upon the white road and set off briskly for the town, my Plan guiding me like a big bright beacon.

What I meant to do—what I was meaning and wanting at this present moment to do—is this.

Being now at Amboise, having knocked up the

hotel porter on arriving, I shall let poor old Almond sleep the sleep of the just until the earliest crack of dawn. Then I shall wake him, have my Napier got ready—if that hasn't been done overnight—pay him, press an extra tip into his not unwilling palm, pack him off to England, home, and beauty, after which I shall romp back to the sleeping farmhouse on my own good car.

My story to Miss Randolph will be that while in Blois yesterday I heard from my master. He is called back to England in a great hurry, wants to leave his car, and would be delighted to let it out on hire at reasonable terms if driven by a good, responsible man—like me. I suppose I shall have to name a sum—say a louis a day—or she'll suspect some game.

She is sure to snatch at a chance, as a drowning man at a straw, and I pat myself on the back for my inspiration. I am looking forward to a new lease of life with the Napier.

The window grows grey; I must call Almond. How the Plan works out you shall hear in my next. *Au revoir*, then.

Your more than ever excited friend,
Jack Winston.

MOLLY RANDOLPH TO HER FATHER

AMBOISE,
November Something-or-Other.

Dear old Lamb,

Did you know that you were the papa of a chameleon? An eccentric combination. But Aunt Mary says she has found out that I am one—a chameleon, I mean; but I don't doubt she thinks me an "eccentric combination" too. And, anyway, I don't see how I can help being changeable. Circumstances and motor-cars rule dispositions.

I wrote you a long letter from Blois, but little did I think then—no, *that* isn't the way to begin. I believe my starting-handle must have gone wrong, to say nothing of my valves—I mean nerves.

Last night we broke down at the other end of nowhere, and rather than desert Mr. Micawber, alias the automobile, I decided to stop till next morning at a wayside farmhouse—the sort of place, as Aunt Mary said, "where anything might happen."

Of course, I needn't have stayed. The Frenchman I told you about in my last letter offered to take us and some of our luggage on to Amboise on his little car; but I didn't feel like saying "yes" to that proposal, and I was sorry for poor Brown, who had worked like a Trojan. Besides, to stay

was an adventure. Monsieur Talleyrand stopped
too, and we had quite a nice supper in a big farm
kitchen, but not as big as the room which the people
gave Aunt Mary and me—a very decent room, with
two funny high beds in it. I couldn't sleep much,
because of remorse about something I had done.
I'm ashamed to tell you what, but you needn't
worry, for it only concerns the car. And then
I didn't know in the least how we were to get on
again next day, as this time the automobile had
taken measures to secure itself a good long rest.

I'd dropped off to sleep after several hours of
staring into the dark and wondering if Brown by
some inspiration would get us out of our scrape,
when a hand, trying to find my face, woke me up.
"It's come!" I thought. "They're going to murder
us." And I was just on the point of shrieking with
all my might to Brown to save me, when I realized
that the hand was Aunt Mary's; it was Aunt Mary's
voice also saying, in a sharp whisper, "What's that?
What's that?"

"That," I soon discovered, was a curious sound
which I suppose had roused Aunt Mary, and sent
her bounding out of bed, like a baseball, in her old
age. I forgot to tell you that in one corner of our
room, behind a calico curtain, was a queer, low
green door, which we had wondered at and tried to
open, but found locked. Now the sound was coming
from behind that door. It was a scuffling and stum-
bling of feet, and a creepy, snorting noise.

Even I was frightened, but it wouldn't do, on
account of discipline, to let Aunt Mary guess. I

just sort of formed a hollow square, told myself
that my country expected me to do my duty, jumped
up, found matches, lighted our one candle, and with
it the lamp of my own courage. That burned so
brightly, I had presence of mind to take the key out
of the other door and try it in the mysterious green
lock. It didn't fit, but it opened the door; and what
do you think was on the other side? Why, a ladder-
like stairway, leading down into darkness. But it
was only the darkness of the family stable, and
instead of beholding our landlord and landlady
digging a grave for us in a business-like manner,
as Aunt Mary fully expected, we saw two cows and
a horse, and three of those silly, surprised-looking
French chickens which are always running across
roads under our automobile's nose.

This was distinctly a relief. We locked the door,
and laid ourselves down to sleep once more. But—
for me—that was easier said than done. I lay
staring into blackness, thinking of many things, until
the blackness seemed to grow faintly pale, the way
old Mammy Luke's face used to turn ashy when she
was frightened at her own slave stories, which she
was telling me. The two windows took form, like
grey ghosts floating in the dark, and I knew dawn
must be coming; but as I watched the squares
growing more distinct, so that I was sure I saw and
didn't imagine them, a light sprang up. It wasn't
the dawn-light, but something vivid and sudden.
I was bewildered, for I'd been in a dozy mood.
I flew up, all dazed and stupid, to patter across
the cold, painted floor on my poor little bare feet.

Our room overlooked the courtyard, and there, almost opposite the window where I stood, a great column of intense yellow flame was rising like a fountain of fire—straight as a poplar, and almost as high. I never saw anything so strange, and I could hardly believe that it wasn't a dream, until a voice seemed to say inside of me, "Why, it's *your car that's on fire!*"

In half a second I was sure the voice was right, and at once I was quite calm. How the car could have got on fire of its own accord was a mystery, unless it had spontaneous combustion, like that awful old man of Dickens, who burnt up and left a greasy black smudge; but there was no time to think, and I only kept saying to myself, as I hurried to slip on a few clothes (the sketchiest toilet I ever made, just a mere outline), how lucky it was that my automobile stood in the courtyard where there was no roof, instead of being in the barn, like Monsieur Talleyrand's. And I knew that Brown slept in the barn, so that, if it had happened there, he might have been burnt to death in his sleep, which made me feel as if I should have to faint away, even to imagine.

But I didn't faint. I tore out of the room, as soon as I was dressed, with my long, fur-lined motoring coat over my "nighty," and yelled "Fire!" at the top of my lungs. But I forgot to yell in French, so of course the farm people couldn't have understood what was the matter, unless they'd seen the light from their windows. It was still dark in the shut-up house, but somehow I found my way downstairs, and to the door by which we'd all come trooping in the evening before. Nobody had appeared yet (though I fancied I heard Aunt Mary's frantic voice), so I concluded that the farmer and his wife must be outside in the fields about their day's work, for these French peasants rise with the dawn, or before it.

I pulled open the door, and the light of the fire struck right at my eyes, which had got used to the darkness in the passage. There was the pillar of fire, as bright and straight and amazingly high as ever, not a trace of the car to be seen in the midst; but silhouetted against the yellow screen of flame was a tall black figure which I recognized as Brown's. He was standing still, looking calmly on, *actually with his hands in his pockets*, instead of trying to put out the fire, and I was dumbfounded, for always before he had shown himself so resourceful.

I stood still, too, a minute, for I *was* surprised. Aunt Mary was having hysterics in one of our windows which she'd thrown open; and Monsieur Talleyrand had come close behind me, it seemed, though I didn't know that then.

I heard the queer clucking and roaring of the fire which was drinking gallons of petrol, but the only thing I *really* thought of was Brown with his hands in his pockets while my car was burning up. I didn't love it—at least I hadn't, and the night before I had behaved to it not at all in a gentlemanly manner, but I couldn't have stood by like that to watch it die without moving a finger.

"Oh, Brown!" I gasped out, running to him, so close that the fire was hot on my face. "Oh, Brown,

how *can* you? Anybody would think that you were
glad."

"And he is!" cried a voice in French at my back.
"It was he who set your automobile on fire, mademoiselle. I myself, who tell you, saw him do it."
I whisked round, and there stood Monsieur Talleyrand, looking very picturesque in an almost theatrical
deshabille, with the firelight shining on him, just as if
it were a scene on the stage.

Brown faced round too, and at the same instant,
the fire having drunk the last drop of petrol, the
flame suddenly died down, and there fell a curious
silence after the roaring of the fire, which had been
like a blast. The woodwork of the car, the hood
and the upper part, as well as the wooden wheels,
had all disappeared—the flame had swallowed and
digested them. Of my varnished and dignified car
there remained only a heap of twisted bits of iron,
glowing a dull red. In the grey dawn we must have
looked like witches at some secret and unholy rite.
The going out of the light had an odd effect upon
us three. When Monsieur Talleyrand launched his
accusation at Brown, he had thrown up his chin, and
the light, striking on his eyeballs, made them glow
like red sparks. But with the dying of the light, the
flash in his eyes died too; and his face changed
to a disagreeable, ashy grey. At the same minute,
when I turned to Brown, it was *his* eyes that glowed,
but the light seemed to come from inside.

I forget whether I ever told you that Brown is
a very good-looking fellow, too good-looking for
a mere *chauffeur*. His face is like his name—

brown; his eyes are brown too, and they can almost speak. One can't help noticing these things, even in one's *chauffeur*. If he weren't a *chauffeur*, one might certainly take him for a gentleman. Some things really are a pity! But never mind.

Brown looked at Monsieur Talleyrand and then he said, "You are a liar." Oh, my goodness, I expected murder!

Monsieur Talleyrand gave a sort of leap.

"Scoundrel, hog, *canaille!*" he stammered, trembling all over. "To be insulted by an English cad, a common *chauffeur*, that a gentleman cannot call out, an incendiary——"

But here Brown broke in with a "Silence!" that made me jump. And the funny part was that it was *he* who looked the gentleman, and Monsieur Talleyrand the cad—quite a little, mean cad, though he is really handsome, with eyelashes you'd have to measure with a tape. That awful "Silence!" seemed to blow his words down his throat like a gust of wind, and while he was getting breath Brown followed up his first shot; but this time it was aimed my way.

"Do you believe what that coward says?" he flung at me, without even taking hold of the words with "Miss" for a handle. Between the two men and the excitement, I gasped instead of answering, and perhaps he took silence for consent, though that is such an old-fashioned theory, especially when it concerns girls. Anyway, he seemed to grow three or four inches taller, and his chin got squarer. "So far from burning your car," said he (and you could have made a block of ice out of each word), "I have been to Amboise to hire a car for you, and thought I had been lucky in securing my old master's,

"As this expedition has occupied the whole night. I have really had no time for plotting, even if there had been a motive, or if I were the sort of man for such work. I hoped you knew I wasn't. But there"—and he pointed to the road outside the open gate—"is my master's car, and the motor is still hot enough to prove——"

"I don't want it to prove," I found breath to exclaim. "Of course, I know you didn't burn my car——"

"But if I say I saw him," cut in Monsieur Talley-rand.

"Pooh!" said I. It was the only word I could think of that went "to the spot," and I hurried on to Brown. "All I minded was seeing you with your hands in your pockets. It didn't seem like you."

"You don't understand," said he. "Just as I opened the doors to drive in the car I'd brought, I saw at a glance that there was something queer about yours. The front seat was off; and as I came nearer I found the screw had been taken out of the petrol tank. With that I caught sight of a flame creeping along a tightly twisted piece of cotton waste—the stuff one cleans cars with. Then I knew that someone had planned to set fire to the car and leave himself time to escape. I sprang at it to knock away the waste, but I was too late. That instant the vapour caught, and I was helpless to do any good, because sand, and a huge lot of it, was the only thing that might have put the fire out, if one could have got it, and then gone near enough to throw it on. Since there was none, the only thing to do was to stand by; and as I'd scorched my hands a little, I suppose I instinctively put them in my pockets."

Monsieur Talleyrand laughed. "You tell your story very well," said he, "but——"

He didn't get farther than that "but," for just then up came running the farmer and his wife from the fields, where they had seen the flames. They began chattering shrilly, in a dreadful state about their buildings, but Brown quieted them down, pointing out that no harm had been done to anything of theirs, and that the fire was out. "Now," he said, "since I didn't burn the car, who did?"

I looked at Monsieur Talleyrand because Brown was looking at him, or rather glaring, when suddenly a loud exclamation from the farmer and his wife made me turn to see what was going to happen next. What I saw was the most wonderful old figure hobbling out of the house, through the door I'd left open—a mere knotted thread of an old thing, in a red flannel nightgown, I think it must have been, and a few streaks of grey hair hanging from a night-cap that tied up its flabby chin. It was the old woman who had breathed so much in the dark the night before; and no wonder they exclaimed at see-ing her crawling out of doors, hardly dressed.

Somehow I felt frightened; she was just like a witch—horrifying, but pathetic too, so old, so little life left in her. She would have come hobbling on into the courtyard, but the farmer stopped her; and there she stood on the door-sill, raising herself up and up on her stick, until suddenly she clutched the farmer's arm and pointed the stick straight at Monsieur Talleyrand, gabbling out something which I couldn't understand.

The farmer had just been going to hustle her inside the house, but he changed his mind. "She says *you* set fire to the automobile," he exclaimed; "she saw it from the window. She thinks you will murder us all. Monsieur, my mother has still her senses. She does not tell foolish lies. You must go out of my house."

"Monstrous!" cried Monsieur Talleyrand. "Am I to be accused on the word of a crazy old witch? I advise you to be careful what you say."

"Here is something else, which speaks for itself," Brown said. "Look!" and he pointed to the ground not far from the gnawed bones of my car. We looked, and saw some wisps of the stuff he had called cotton-waste, twisted up and saturated with oil. "That was used to fire the petrol," he went on. "There was none like it on our car, but you carried plenty in yours. I've seen you use it, and so, I think, has Miss Randolph."

For an instant Talleyrand seemed to be taken aback, and he looked so pale in the dim light that I was almost going to be sorry for him, when with a sudden inspiration he struck an attitude before me. He had the air of ignoring the others, forgetting that they existed.

"Mademoiselle," he said in a low, really beautiful

voice, that might have drawn tears from an audience if he had been the leading man cruelly mistaken for a neighbouring villain, "*chère mademoiselle*, I did what these *canaille* accuse me of. Yes, I did it! But they cannot understand why. Only you are high enough to understand. It was—because of my great love for you. All is to be forgiven to such love. Cheerfully, a hundred times over, will I pay for this material damage I have done. I am not poor, except in lacking your love. To gain an opportunity of winning it, to take you from your brutal *chauffeur*, who is not fit to have delicate ladies trusted to his care, I did what I have done, meaning to lay my car, myself, all that I have and am, figuratively at your feet."

If he had really, instead of "figuratively," I'm sure I couldn't have resisted kicking him, which would have been unladylike. How *could* I ever have thought he was nice? Ugh! I could have strangled him with his own eyelashes! Brown was right about him, after all. I wonder why it doesn't please one more to find out that other people are right?

"I don't want you to pay," said I. "I only want you to go away."

I've a dim impression that I emphasised these words with a gesture, and that he seized my hand before I could pull it back. I also have a dim impression of exclaiming, "Oh, Brown!" in a frightened voice—just as silly as if I'd been an early-Victorian female. I wished I hadn't, but it was too late. Brown, evoked, was not so easily revoked. A whirlwind seemed to catch Monsieur Talleyrand up, but it was really Brown. They went together to visit a disagreeable, shiny green pond in the middle of the farmyard. Brown stopped at the brink; but Monsieur Talleyrand didn't stop—I suspect Brown knew why. He went on, and in. And, oh, Dad! to save my life, I couldn't help laughing. All my excitement and everything went into that laugh—the half-crying kind I used to call the "boo-higgles" when I was a little girl—you remember?

I was afraid the wretch might hear me, so I turned and fairly ran for the house. Brown took some long steps, and reached me before I got there, apparently not the least concerned in the splashing sounds which so much interested everybody else.

"About my master's car, miss," said he coolly. "Will you have it? He was at Amboise. I'd heard from him there, that if I knew of anyone wanting to hire a car, his was in the market for the next few weeks, as he was suddenly called away, and didn't want to take it. It's a good car—the best I ever drove—and he's willing to let it go cheap, as he trusts me to drive, and it's an accommodation to him."

"Oh, I'm delighted to have it," I answered, not stopping to ask the price, because details didn't seem to matter at that moment. "It's—it's just like the ram caught in the bushes, isn't it? And—I don't know how to thank you enough for everything." I can't tell exactly what I meant by that, except that I meant a lot.

"There's nothing to thank me for, miss," said Brown, quite respectful again; but a queer little smile lurked in the corners of his mouth. "You must be hungry," he remarked. "Shall I ask them to have breakfast prepared by the time you're—ready?"

I believe he was going to say "dressed," and stopped for fear of hurting my feelings. I only stayed long enough to throw a "Yes, please," over my shoulder. But when I was upstairs with Aunt Mary, my face feeling rather hot, I didn't begin to make my toilet; I went and "peeked" out of the window.

That unspeakable Frenchman was shaking himself like a big dog, and sneaking towards the house, with the farmer at his heels. The farmer was a big fellow, and dependable; still, I ran and locked the door. I suppose the Beast finished dressing and packed his bag. I heard nothing; but half an hour later (I'd bathed and dressed like lightning, for once), when we were just sitting down to breakfast, and Brown had come into the room to ask a question, there was a light pattering on the stairs; the front door opened, and somebody went out. Two minutes later came the whirring of a motor, and I jumped up.

"Oh, Brown!" I exclaimed, "if he should have taken *your* car!"

"No fear of that," said Brown. "I know the sound just as I know one human voice from another. That's his Pieper. It's all right."

Still I wasn't at ease. "But he may have done something bad to yours. He's capable of anything," I said. "Do let's go and see."

Brown flushed up a little. "I'll go," he said. He was off on the word, racing across the farmyard. I couldn't eat my breakfast till he came back, which he

did in a few minutes. I knew by his face before he
spoke that something was wrong. "I was a fool to
leave the car for even a second till he was out of the
way," said the poor fellow. "Every tyre gashed.
No doubt he'd have liked to smash up the car altogether if he'd had time, but his object was to do his
worst and get off scot free. He's done both. It's
thanks to you and your quick thought that the
damage is so small."

"If it hadn't been for me he wouldn't have been
here," I almost wept. "Now we're delayed again
just when I began to hope that all might be well."

"All shall be well," answered Brown encouragingly.
"We'll go 'on the rims' as far as Amboise."

I didn't know what it was to go on the rims, but
when we'd settled up with the farmer, and I'd said
a last, long good-bye to my car's bones (which I made
the landlord a present of), I found out. It's something like "going on your uppers." I don't need to
explain that, do I? But the car is such a beauty
that seeing it with its tyres *en déshabille* seemed an
indignity. Brown couldn't help showing his pride
in it, and I don't wonder. He is certainly a "Mascot"
to me, for he has got me out of every scrape I've
been in since he "crossed my path," as the melo-
dramas say. And now this lovely car! On the way
to Amboise he told me what it was to be let for.
Only twenty francs a day. I protested, because
Rattray had said that good cars couldn't be hired for
less than twenty *pounds* a week; but Brown explained
that this was because his master liked him to drive it,
and that really it wasn't so cheap as I thought.

suppose it's all right. Funny, though, that I should
have the car of that Mr. John Winston, whose mother
—Lady Brighthelmston—I met in Paris, and promised to meet again in Cannes. Fancy Aunt Mary
and me lolling luxuriously (I love that word "lolling")
in a snow-white car with scarlet cushions, all the brass-
work gleaming like a fireman's helmet—the rakiest,
smartest car imaginable! There are two seats in
front and a roomy *tonneau* behind. The steering and
other arrangements are quite different from those in
the poor dead Dragon—rest its wicked soul! There's
a steering-wheel, and below it two ducky little han-
dles that do everything. One's the "advance spark-
ing lever," the other the "mixture lever." There are
no horrid belts to break themselves—and your heart
at the same time, but instead a "change speed gear"
and a "clutch." I had my first lesson in driving,
sitting by Brown on the way to Amboise. He
teaches one awfully well, and I was perfectly happy
learning, especially when I found that the faster we
went the easier the dear thing is to steer. I was so
interested that I didn't know a bit what the road was
like, except that it was good and white and mostly
level, so that when Brown suddenly said "There is
the Château of Amboise," I was quite startled.

Luckily he was driving again by that time, or I
should probably have shot us into the river instead
of turning to the bridge; for we were on the other
side of the Loire looking across to the castle.

You poor, dear, stay-at-home Dad, to think of your
never having seen any of these lovely places that
you've nobly sent me to browse among! You say

you admire Wall Street more than French châteaux,
and that when you want a grand view you can go
and look at Brooklyn Bridge or the statue of Liberty
by night; but you don't know what you're missing.
And if travelling would *really* bore you, why do you
like me to describe things, so that I can "give you a
picture though my eyes"?

I wonder if girls who have lived all their lives in
old, old countries can have the same sort of awed,
surprised, almost dream-like feeling that comes to me
when I see these great feudal castles that are like
history in stone? Yes, in stone, and yet the stone
seems *alive* too as if it were the *flesh* of history; and
as I think of all the things that have happened
behind the splendid walls, I can hear history's heart
beating as if it and the world were young with me.

This château country of the Loire must be one of
the most interesting spots on earth, centring as it
did the old Court life of France, and Brown says it
really is so. He has travelled tremendously and
remembers everything, though he *is* nothing but a
chauffeur.

Each place we have come to I have thought must
be the best; but I know that no other castle will
make me take Amboise down off the pedestal I've
set it on, in my mind.

As I glanced up at it in the sunshine the great
white carved *façade* dazzled me. It looked as if it
had been cut out of ivory. The bridge rests on an
island in the middle of the wide, yellow, slow-moving
stream of the Loire, which has a curiously still surface
like ice. Brown drove slowly without my having to

ask. He's wonderful that way. He always knows
what you are feeling, as if you had telegraphed him
the news. And there before us lay the little town of
Amboise, sprinkled along the river-bank as if each
house were a votive offering on the shrine of the
Château towering above on its plateau of rock.

I couldn't make out the architecture at first. The
castle was just a vast, dazzling complication of enormous round towers, bastions, terraces, balconies, and
crenellations. Oh, those balconies! Instantly I could
see poor little fainting Queen Mary held up by wicked
Catherine de Medici—the record wickedest mother-
in-law of history—to watch the execution of the
Huguenots. And then the row of heads hanging
from the balcony afterwards, like terrible red gargoyles! When we went into the Château later the
custodian, or whatever you call him, showed us where
the fine ironwork was stained and rusted with the
Huguenots' blood.

I was very angry with Aunt Mary because she
kept her nose in her Baedeker, and preferred reading
about the castle to seeing it when she had the chance.
I have my opinion of people who won't take their
Baedeker in doses either before or after meals of
sight-seeing; but Aunt Mary spreads it so thick over
hers that what's underneath is lost.

We drove to a nice little hotel tucked away at the
foot of the Château, for *déjeuner*, and to get rid
of our luggage, for we'd have to stop at Amboise
till the four new tyres (which Brown now wired for)
should arrive from Paris. We had so many courses
that I grew quite impatient, for I wanted to be off to

the castle. And to save time I insisted on Brown lunching with us. That's happened before several times, so that it doesn't seem at all strange now, though Aunt Mary fussed at first, and even I felt rather funny. But the queer part is, it's so *much* more difficult to remember that Brown's not a gentleman than to make an effort to be civil to him as if he were one. Rattray at the table was beyond words, and so are a lot of Frenchmen who ought to know better; but—you'll laugh at me—I don't see how a duke could eat any better than Brown, or have nicer hands and nails; though how he does it with the car to clean is more than I can tell.

We came towards the castle, after *déjeuner*, from the back through the town, which was gay with booths and blue blouses and pretty peasant girls, because the market was being held. We went right through the crowd, up, up a sloping path, where suddenly we were in a restful silence, after the chattering and chaffering below. And I felt as if we had got into a novel of Scott's ; for if we'd been his characters he would have brought us up short at a secretive door in a tower, just like the one where we had to knock. One couldn't guess what would be on the other side of that tower; and it was like walking on through the next chapter of the same novel (walking slowly and with dignity, so that we might "live up to" the author of our being) to wander up a steep road leading to a plateau and reach the still, formal garden with the great castle rising out of it.

On this plateau a lovely thing simply took my

eyes captive and wouldn't let them go. It was the most perfect gem of a little chapel out of dreamland. Brown said it was "a jewel of the pure Gothic, one of the most precious of the florid kind in France." Comic to have one's *chauffeur* talking to one like that, isn't it? But I'm used to it now, and feel quite injured if Brown happens not to know something I ask him about.

I never realised what an important lady Anne of Brittany was, till I was introduced to her sweet little ermine at Blois. Brown hinted then that I would keep on realising it more and more as we drove through the Loire country, and so I do. This chapel was hers—built for her, and I envy her having it. Couldn't you, Dad dear, just make a bid, and have it taken over for our garden at Lennox? But no! that would be sacrilege. It's almost sacrilege even to joke about it. Yet, oh, that carving of St. Hubert and his holy stag over the door! I've no jewellery so lovely as that cameo in stone; and I've got to leave it behind in Europe.

Poor Charles the Eighth, too, seemed to come to us like a human, every day young man one knew when we saw the low doorway where he knocked his head and killed himself, running in a great hurry to play tennis. How little he guessed when he started that he should never have that game, and why! I wonder if Anne was sorry when he died, or if she liked having another wedding and being a queen all over again when she married Louis the Twelfth?

I should have thought more about the ladies' love

affairs, only I got so interested in an *oubliette*, and in a perfectly Titanic round tower, with an inclined plane corkscrewing up, round and round inside it, so broad and so gradual that horses and carriages used in old, old days to be driven from the town-level up to the top. "Only think what fun, Brown," I couldn't help saying, "if we could drive the *car* up here!" "The idea!" sniffed Aunt Mary. "As if they'd allow such a thing!" But Brown didn't answer; he just looked thoughtfully at the gradient.

We went up, too, on the top of one of the great towers of the castle itself, and it was glorious to stand there looking away over the windings of the river. We were at a bend midway between Blois and Tours, and ever so far off we could see two little horns sticking up over the undulations of the land. They were the towers of the cathedral of Tours; and in that same direction Brown showed me a queer thing like a long, thin finger pointing at the sky—the Lanterne of Rochecorbon. They used to flash signals from it all the way to Amboise, and so on to Blois, when any horror happened with which they were particularly pleased, like a massacre of Huguenots.

Now, most patient gentleman, at last I've finished my harangue. I'm ashamed to think how long it is, but I'm writing wrapped up in a warm coat, under a *tilleul* in the Château garden, where I've been allowed to bring my campstool. Do you know what a *tilleul* is? I don't believe you do. I didn't till the other day; but I shan't tell you, except that the

very name suggests to me leisured ease and sauntering courtiers. You must come over to France and
find out—and incidentally fetch me home—only not
yet, please, oh, not yet. As for the *tilleul*, if you've
any romance left in your dear old body you'd love
sitting under it, even in winter. If it were summer,
with the limes in blossom—well, the best way to express my feeling is to remark that if, in June moonlight, under a *tilleul*, a man I hated should propose to
me, I'd believe for the moment I loved him and say
"Yes—yes!" But you need not be frightened; it
isn't summer or moonlight, and there's no man except
Brown within a hundred miles of your silly

MOLLY.

MOLLY RANDOLPH TO HER FATHER

Three days since I wrote, blessed old Thing, but it seems three times three, for all the hours have been as cramfull as you used to fill my stocking at Christmas.

We couldn't get away from Amboise, as we expected, because the tyres didn't arrive till late in the evening. I knew it must be a long, tedious business fixing them on, so I never dreamed of starting next morning; but when morning came, and with it the chambermaid and my bath, there was a note from Brown, written in a hand a lot nicer than my poor "fist," announcing that the car was ready, and if I would like a surprise, might he "respectfully suggest" that I should come downstairs as soon as possible. You can imagine that I didn't "stand on the order of my going." My hair crinkled with surprise at being done so quickly, and I was in such a hurry that I nearly—but not quite—slid down the balusters.

Brown was at the front door, with the car all politely polished, and seeming to stand upon tiptoe on its big new tyres. But smart as the car was, it was nothing to the *chauffeur*. He looked like a sort of male Cinderella just after the fairy godmother had waved her wand; only instead of a ball dress she had given him, in place of his black leather, a suit of grey clothes; one of those high, turnover collars I love on a good-looking man; a dark necktie, and what *we* call a "Derby" hat and the English call a "bowler." He was nice! I don't know if I'm a judge of a man's clothes, but to me they seemed as good form as any tailor in the world could cut. Perhaps the Honourable John gave them to him. Poor dear! he's far too fine a fellow really to have to wear another man's cast-off garments; but I suppose Providence must know best, and, anyhow, I'm sure the H. J. never looked half as nice in the things.

Brown had on also a mysterious air, which seemed to go with the clothes, and he asked if I'd mind taking a short run with him, without knowing beforehand where I was going. I said that, on the contrary, I should *like* it. That seemed to please him. He helped me in (not that I needed it), the car started with a touch, and we began to thread the streets of the town behind the Château, I wondering *what* was going to happen. When I had been in this car before, it was to travel "on the rims," you know. Now, on our four-plump new Michelins from Paris it was like being in a balloon, so easy was the motion even over the badly paved streets.

We wound round under the high wall of the Château, and came in a few minutes to a huge gateway. As we slowed down this gateway opened mysteriously from within to show a dim corkscrew of a road winding upward. I opened my mouth to

ask an astonished question; then I thought better
of it and kept still, though I know my eyes must
have been snapping when Brown actually drove the
car in. The gateway clanged behind us, as if by
enchantment, shutting us into a twilight region, and
behold, we were mounting the incline of the great
tower. up which, perhaps, nobody had ever driven
since the days of Mary Stuart.

Wasn't it *kind* of Brown to remember my wish
(which even I had forgotten!) to drive up the tower?
I could hardly thank him enough for such a new
and thrilling sensation as it was, twisting up and up,
seeming to float in the vast hollow of the passage,
the exquisite carved and vaulted roof giving back
a rythmical reverberation of the throbbing of our
motor.

I couldn't even say "thank you," though, except
in my thoughts, till we got to the top (which we did
much too soon), for somehow it would have broken
the charm to speak. But I think Brown understood
that I appreciated it all, and what he had done.

At the top a big doorway stood open, and by it
one of the delightful, grizzled, dignified old dears
who must have been made guardians of the Château,
because they fit so well into the picture. I thought,
though, that this one looked different from before,
for some reason quite flurried and almost scared.
I suppose it must have been the car and the unusual-
ness that upset him; but Brown drove out splendidly,
stopping in the terrace-garden.

"At that door," said the charming old fellow,
"Francis the First of France received Henry the

Eighth of England, who with a train of a hundred knights rode up the sloping way in the tower. To-day is the first time that an automobile has ever been inside the doors; therefore, mademoiselle, you have just been making history." And he bowed so deliciously that I could have cried, because I hadn't my purse with me to give him a "guerdon"; that would have been the only word, if I had had it. Fortunately Brown had. Something yellow glittered as it passed from hand to hand, and the old Frenchman (so dramatic, like most of his countrymen) bowed again and took off his hat with a flourish. If the something hadn't been yellow, but only white, I wonder if he would have let us make that splendid, sweeping circle round the gardens before we plunged back into the cool gloom of the tower?

Oh, that descent! I feel breathless, just remembering it, but it was a glorious kind of breathlessness, like you feel when you go tobogganing—only more so. Brown took it at tremendous speed, but I wasn't a bit afraid, for I trust him utterly as a driver. If he said he could take me safely over Niagara Falls, and looked straight at me in a way he has when he said it, I believe I'd go—unless, of course, you objected!

I found myself thinking of Poe's descent of the Maelström, and when I said so to Brown afterwards, it turned out that he'd read it. He had the car perfectly in hand, and steered it to a hair's breadth. We were down in a moment—or it seemed so; and coming out into the bright little streets was like waking up after a strange dream. In three minutes more we were at the door of our hotel, and I really *was* asking myself if I had dreamed it.

"Brown," said I, "I told you once before that you were a leather angel. Now I believe you are a grey tweed Genie. This has been the nicest morning of my life. But you really must tell me how much you paid that custodian, and let me give you back the money at once."

He interrupted himself in the midst of a beaming smile to wrinkle his eyebrows together. "It's been a nice morning for me, too, miss," said he quite humbly; "but it will half spoil it if you won't let it stand as it is. It was only a few francs, and as you pay me a good screw, I can well afford it. You're always so good, that I know you'd be sorry to hurt my feelings."

Well, of course I would; so I couldn't say any more, could I? Though before all these motor-car wonders began it would have felt odd to take a "treat" from one's servant.

Now, Dad, I'm getting conscience-stricken, and keep wondering with every paragraph (especially what I call my "descriptive" paragraphs) if I'm boring you. I won't give you our daily programme *en masse*. I'll just sum things up by saying that we've simply lived, moved, and had our being in, on, or at castles. This country of the Loire is a sort of fairyland, where everybody had a castle, or at the very least a lordly dwelling-place that was more fortress than private house. You can't look up or down the river but that on every hill you see a château, with enough history clustering about it to make up a fat volume. How they all escaped the Revolution is a marvel. But they have; and if they've been much restored, it is so cleverly done that the most critical eyes are deceived.

If I could live in one of the "show" châteaux, I'd choose Chenonceaux. We drove to it on the day of the Tower, as I've labelled it in my book of memory, "taking it in" on our way to Tours. It's no use your making a note of that wish of mine, though Dad, and trying to buy it, because somebody else has done that already. But if you can find a river as pretty as the Cher (an appropriate name for the little daughter of the Loire, on which—*over* which, literally, Chenonceaux stands), you might build me one on the same pattern, so I'll give you a general idea of what the castle is like.

Let me see, what *is* it like? To make a comparison would be giving to an airy nothing a local habitation and a name. Not that Chenonceaux is *nothing*—quite the opposite; but it leaves in the mind an impression of airiness and gaiety, sweet and elusive as one of those quaint French *chansons* you like me to sing you, with my guitar, on a summer evening. I think, even if I hadn't been told, I should have felt instinctively that it must have been built to please a pretty, capricious woman. If such a woman could be turned into a house, she would look like Chenonceaux, and wouldn't suffer by the change. Perhaps Diane de Poîtiers isn't a proper object of sympathy for a well-brought-up young lady like Chauncy Randolph's daughter; but I can't help pitying her, because that horrid old frump of a Catherine

de Medici grabbed it away from her before Henry the
Second was hardly cold in his grave. Think how
Diane, who had loved the place, must have felt to
fancy that stuffy Catherine in her everlasting black
dresses, squatting in her beautiful rooms! We saw
those rooms, by the way, for we came on one of the
days when people are allowed to go through the
Château (Brown had planned that), and the clever
millionaires who own it have had the sense and the
grace to leave everything just as it was, at least in
Catherine's time. And one can take the bad,
Catherine taste out of one's mouth by thinking of
lovely little Mary Stuart singing like a lark through
the rooms, and living there and in the garden the
happiest days that she was ever to know.

One wouldn't suppose that a gloomy, plotting mind
like Catherine's would have had a place in it for
creating beauty; but it had its one ornamental
corner, or she couldn't have thought out the bridge-
gallery thrown across the Cher, springing from the
original building and spanning the river to the farther
shore.

There are two storeys over the bridge, long corridors, all windows, and lovely green and gold
river lights, netted over the floors and walls—the
most exquisite effect. I walked there, calling up the
spirits of vanished queens and princesses—the "dear,
dead women," seeing "all the gold that used to fall
and hang about their shoulders." Oh, I've got the
quotation wrong, but it's Aunt Mary's fault, for at
this very minute she's reading aloud to herself in a
guide-book about Rousseau and a lot of other shining

lights who used to visit Chenonceaux when it be-longed to Monsieur and Madame Dupin; but those days were comparatively modern, so I don't take much interest.   Nothing at Chenonceaux seems worth while unless it happened before the days of Charles the Ninth.

Tours looked at first sight very sedate and grey, after Chenonceaux, for the airy picture of the castle had kept floating before my eyes during our run.   It seems to me we are always on the other side of the river from things, and have to get to them by cross-ing long bridges.   We did it again at Tours, and it was particularly long, and very fine.   But it was evening, and dim and bitterly cold; and I'm afraid I shouldn't have paid as much attention to it as I did if Brown hadn't said that Balzac called it "one of the finest monuments of France."   And then in a minute, at the entrance to the town, we saw two ghostly white statues glimmering in a wide, green *place*.   "There, miss, are the two tutelary geniuses of this part of France," said Brown; "Rabelais and Descartes."   By that time we had flashed past, but I screwed my neck round to look back at them till I got a "crick" in it.   Have you ever noticed that most of the things people tell you to look at, or that you particularly want to see in life, are always be-hind your back or on one side, as if to give you the greatest possible trouble?   It seems as if there must be a "moral in it," as Alice's Duchess would have said.

Tours appeared *that* evening (I have a motive for the emphasis) to consist of one long, straight street;

and turning to the left at the end, we pulled up at the door of a hotel. Just an ordinary-looking hotel it was on the outside, and I little thought what my impressions of it would be by-and-by.

I was tired, not so much physically from what we had done, but with the feeling that my capacity for admiring and enjoying things had been filled up and brimmed over, so that a drop more in would actually hurt. Do you know that sensation? It was just the mood to appreciate warmth and cosiness. We got both. Aunt Mary and I had two bedrooms opening off a sitting-room; dear, old-fashioned rooms, and, above all, *French* old-fashioned, which to me is fascinating. We made ourselves as pretty as Nature ordained us severally to be, and went downstairs. The dining-room was our first big surprise. It was almost worthy of one of the châteaux, with its dignified tapestried and wainscotted walls, and its big, branching candelabra. I'm sure if we'd been dining at a château we shouldn't have got a better dinner. I don't think anything ever tasted so good to me in my life, and I couldn't help wondering how poor, tired Brown was faring while we lazy ones feasted in state in the *salle à manger*. I thought of you, too, for you would have loved the things to eat. They were rich and Southern, and tasted in one's mouth just the way the word "Provence" sounds in one's ear. Aunt Mary had read in one of her ubiquitous guide-books that Touraine as well as Provence is famous for its "succulent cooking," and for once a guide-book seems to be right. They had all sorts of tricky, rich little dishes for dinner—

rillettes and other things which would have made
your mouth water (though if it did, and I were by,
I'd shut my eyes), and the head waiter told me when
I asked, that they were specialties of Tours and of
the hotel. I think *he* must be a specialty of Tours
and the hotel too. He has the softest, most engaging,
yet dignified manner; and the way he has of setting
down a dish before you seems to season it and give
you a double appetite. There's another man in the
hotel, too, who adds to the "aroma"; he's like a
"bush to wine," or something I've heard you say.
By day he's *valet de chambre*, in a scarlet waistcoat
no brighter than his cheeks and eyes; at dinner
he's a waiter in correct "dress" clothes, and then
he goes back to valeting again till midnight. He
would put me in a good temper if I had started
out to murder someone, and when he brought us the
wine list, waiting with a cherry-cheeked smile to see
what we would choose, nothing seemed worthy of
him except champagne; but champagne looked so
dissipated for two lone females. However, I had
decided to have some, to drink the health of the
new car, and perhaps—a little—to shock Aunt Mary,
when the diamond-eyed one respectfully inquired,
in nice Southern French, how we would like to try
a "little wine of the country, sparkling Vouvray;
quite a ladies' wine." So we compromised with
Vouvray It was too ridiculously cheap, but it had
a delicious flavour, and Aunt Mary and I, being
merely females, agreed that it was more delicate than
any champagne we had ever tasted. We drank your
health and the car's, and then I had a sudden inspi-

ration. "To the 'Lightning Conductor'!" said I,
raising my glass.

"What lightning conductor? And what do you
mean?" inquired Aunt Mary.

"The one and only Lightning Conductor—Brown,"
I explained. "I have just thought of that as a good
name for him, now that he has a chance to spin us
across the world at such a pace with a new car."

"I do hope, my dear Molly," severely remarked
Aunt Mary, setting down her glass with an indignant
little thud, "you will not call that young man any
such thing to his face. He has already been allowed
far too many liberties, and though I must say he has
not to any great extent taken undue advantage of
them so far, he may *break out* at any moment."

I'm sorry to tell you, Dad, that I said "Pooh!"
and asked her if she thought Brown were an active
volcano. Anyway, whether I call him so "to his
face" or not, the "Lightning Conductor" he is, and
will remain for me, though perhaps he wouldn't be
flattered at being "launched and christened" with
mere Vouvray.

I didn't expect to like Tours half as much as I
do. But we have been here for three days, and
though I thought at first there was only one long
street, we've found something interesting to see
every hour of daylight—so I write in the evenings
in our cosy sitting-room. Or if I don't write, I read
Balzac. I never appreciated him as I do here, on
his "native heath." I have begged Brown to name
his master's car "Balzac," because it, too, is a "violent and complicated genius," I've gazed at the

house where Balzac was born; I've photographed the Balzac medallion; I've stuffed my trunks with illustrated editions of Balzac's books; and I've gone to see everything I could find, which he ever spoke about. His *Curé de Tours* is the most harrowing story I ever read; and the strange little house in the shadow of the cathedral, with one of the great buttresses planting its enormous foot in the wee garden, fascinates me. There lived the horrible Mademoiselle Gamard, and there, with her, lodged the wicked Curé, and the poor, good little Curé, over whose childlike, gentle stupidity and agony I half cried my eyes out last night. But Balzac's French discourages me. He must have had a wonderful vocabulary. I am always finding words on every page which I never saw before.

I don't like cathedrals much as a rule, unless there's something really extraordinary about them; but I love the big, grey, Gothic cathedral of Tours. It seems a different grey from any other, not cold and forbidding, but warm and very soft, as if it were made of sealskin. I suppose that is partly the effect of the beautiful carvings of the tall, tall front. I feel as if I should like to smooth and caress it with my hand. And it is beautiful inside. Somehow it is so individual that it gives you a welcome, as if it meant to be your friend.

The streets of *old* Tours are so intricate that Aunt Mary and I would never have known where to go, but Brown, who has been here before, has guided us everywhere. He took us to see the house of Tristan the Hermit, and an adorable little convent,

which is called the Petit St. Martin, with lovely
Renaissance carving, and actually a *tilleul* He
showed us the oldest house in Tours, the quaintest
building you could imagine, standing on a corner,
with lots of other very old houses on the same street.
And the Charlemagne Tower—I'm not sure, but I
liked that the best of all—and a marvellous fourteenth-
century house, a perfect lacework of carving, which
has been restored, and is called the Maison Gouin,
after the rich man who lives in it. Oh, I forgot to
tell you, I have bought your favourite *Quentin
Durward*, and am sandwiching him with Balzac.
Reading him over again in this country was Brown's
idea for me, and I'm obliged to him for the "tip."
Speaking of tips reminds me I really ought to give
him one—a very large one, I'm sure, And yet it
will be awkward offering it, I'm afraid. I know I
shall stammer and be an idiot generally; but I shall
prop my courage with the reflection that, after all,
he *is* a *chauffeur*, and perhaps has, in his heart, been
wondering why I haven't given him anything before.

Yesterday I saw palm trees, growing in the *place*,
and kissed my hand to them, because they told
me that we were on the threshold of the South.
Another thing in Tours which suggests the South,
I think, is the *patisserie*. Aunt Mary and I have
discovered a confectioner's to conjure with; but
Tours seems to have discovered him long ago, for
all the " beauty and fashion " of the town go there
for coffee and cakes in the afternoon. We do likewise—when we have time ; and yesterday Aunt
Mary ate twelve little cakes, each one different from

the other. You see, they are so good, and she said, as a conscientious tourist, she thought she ought to try every kind in the shop, so as to know which was nicest. But she felt odd afterwards, and refused one or two of the best courses at dinner.

The way that we have used our time at Tours is very much to our credit, I think—or rather to the Lightning Conductor's. In the mornings Brown has taken us on excursions outside the town, and in the afternoons, before dark, we have "done" the town itself, as Aunt Mary would say, though I hate the expression myself. But one whole day out of our three we spent in running with the car to Langeais and Azay-le-Rideau.

That new car is a treasure, and Brown drives as if there were a sort of *sympathy* between him and it. We go at a thrilling pace sometimes, but that is only when we have a long, straight road, empty as far as the eye can see. He is very considerate to "horse-drivers," as he calls them, and he says "for the sake of the sport" everyone driving an automobile should be careful of the rights of other persons on the road. He slows down at once, or even stops the car altogether, if we meet a restive horse. Once he got out and pacified a silly beast that was nervous, leading it past the car, and when it was quite quiet the old peasant who was driving exclaimed that if all automobilists were like us there would never be complaints. We managed to make up for lost time, though; and when Brown "lets her out," as he calls it, until we are going as fast as a quick train, I can tell you it is something worth living for. When the country is very beautiful we drive slowly, and save our "spurts" for the uninteresting parts.

I know you've read Balzac's *Duchesse de Langeais*, in English, for it was I who gave it to you. I don't suppose she ever lived, really, at the Château de Langeais or anywhere else; but the thought of her made Langeais even more interesting to me than it would have been if she'd been erased from the picture.

It's a great, grey, frowning, **turreted** and crenelated fortress-house, and I felt so much obliged to it for having kept its practicable drawbridge. We drove almost up to the door, through a clean, very old little town, and just opposite the entrance was a quaint house where Brown said Rabelais had lived. I don't believe Aunt Mary knew anything about Rabelais. However, she eagerly Kodaked the house, and later, when I gravely mentioned to her that Rabelais was the kind you wouldn't allow *me* to read, but of course *she* might, if she liked, she gave a squeak of dismay, and threatened to waste all her films rather than let a photographer see that one when they went to be developed. I do hope *I* shan't be an old maid !

The Parisian millionaire who owns the Château, and lives in it part of the year, must be a wonderfully generous, public-spirited man. Only think, he has spent thousands and thousands in restoring the castle, in keeping up the lovely garden, and in having all the rooms exquisitely furnished and decorated exactly in the period of wicked Louis the Eleventh and Charles the Eighth. But instead of keeping these beautiful things for himself and his family and friends, he lets everybody have the benefit, not even making an exception of his own private rooms. Here Anne of Brittany was very much to the fore again, for she was married to Charles at Langeais, and we went into the room of the wedding. I should have liked to take the splendid, dignified, old major-domo, who showed us about, home with me; but I'm sure he'd pine away and die if torn from his beloved Château.

We bought quaint painted iron brooches, with Anne of Brittany's crest on them, in the town; and then we drove away through pretty, undulating country, which must be lovely in summer, to Azay le-Rideau. Francis the First built it; and he certainly had as good taste in castles as in ladies, which is saying a great deal.

This is a fairy house. It doesn't look as if it had ever been *built* in the ordinary sense, but as if somebody had dropped a huge, glimmering pearl down on the green meadow, and it had rolled near enough to the water to see its own reflection. Then the same somebody had carved exquisite designs all over the pearl, and finally hollowed it out and turned it into a king's house.

As usual, we came to it across a bridge, not spanning the Loire this time, but a branch of the river Indre; and it's in the Indre that the pearly Château bathes its pearly feet. Almost I wished that I hadn't gone inside the pearl. Not that the inside was worthless; there was a mantel or two, and a great show staircase. with a carved. vaulted roof; but it

was an anti-climax after the outside and after Langeais. When we came out from "viewing the interior," as the guide-books say, I walked all round
the Château again, looking up at the carved chimneys
and the sculptured windows, the charming turrets,
and the sloping roof of blue grey slate; all so light
and elegant, seeming to say, "Come and live here.
You will be happy." Oh, they have some lovely
things in Europe, that we can never have in our new
country! We've a good excuse for wanting to come
over here. But it's so good to feel that the things
are for us, and for everybody—not just for England,
or France, or Italy, as the case may be.

To-morrow we are going to try and see three
châteaux—Ussé, and Luynes, and Chinon. We'll
come back to Tours and our dear Hotel de l'Univers;
but the day after—good-bye to both, and how-do-
you-do Loches! I'll leave this open, and put in a
postscript. I haven't given you a real, characteristic
postscript for a long time.

Evening; and LOCHES.

"Here I am again!" as Jack-in-the-Box says.
And we've done all the things I said we were going
to. But I'm too full of Loches and too excited about
Loches to tell you anything of yesterday's three
castles, except to fling them an adjective or two, and
pass on. Let me see, what adjective, since I've confined myself to one, shall I give Ussé? "Splendid,"
I think. "Interesting" is all I can afford for Luynes,
though it deserves a lot more, if only for its history.
And well—"magnificent" must do for Chinon. Per-

haps it has the most beautiful view of all. But
Loches—Loches! I had forgotten its existence till
I dug it up for myself in *Quentin Durward*, and the
guide-books, to which Aunt Mary is so faithful, don't
do it any sort of justice. They don't tell you to go
to see it, *whatever* else you must make up your mind
to miss. Why, Aunt M.'s particular pet devoted
almost as much space to the queer little rock village
of Rochecorbon, whose lighted windows glared at
us like cat's eyes away high up above the road, one
dark evening (when we'd been belated after an excursion) getting back to Tours.

Luckily the Lightning Conductor appreciated
Loches at its true value, and told me it was well
worth making a short détour—as we must—to see.
We had to go out of our way as far as a place called
Cormery, but that was nothing, and yesterday morning early we started. It was the first sparkling blue-
and-gold day we have had for a while; it seemed as
if it must have come across to us from Provence, as
a sample, to show what we might expect if we hurried
on there. The air was like champagne—or Vouvray
—and we spun along at our very best on the smooth,
wide Route Nationale, our faces turned towards
Provence as a graceful compliment for the gift of the
weather.

We have a neat little trick of getting to places just
in time for lunch, and we managed it at Loches, as
usual. We'd hardly driven into the town before
I fell in love with its quaintness; but I didn't fall
in love with the hotel until I'd been surprised with
a perfectly delicious *déjeuner*. Then I let myself go;

and when I'd seen how pretty the old-fashioned bed-rooms were, I begged to stay all night instead of going on. Brown seems to regard my requests as if they were those of royalty—commands; and he re-arranged our programme accordingly. I'm writing in a green-and-pink damask bedroom now, but when I shut my eyes I can see the castle and the dungeons and—Madame César. Yes, I think I can find my way back for your benefit, and return on our own tracks.

First, like a promising preface to the ruined strong-hold of the terrible Louis, we went through a massive gateway, flanked with towers, and climbed up a winding street of ancient, but not decrepit houses, to come cut at last upon a plateau with the gigantic walls of the castle on our left. When I remembered *who* caused those outworks and walls to be put up, so high and grim and strong, and *why*, I felt a little "creep" run up my spine at sight of the enormous mass of stonework. "Who enters here leaves hope behind" might have been written over the gateway in the dreadful days when Loches was in its wicked prime. Those walls are colossal, like perpendicular cliffs. At a door in one of them we tinkled a bell, and presently, with loud unlocking of double doors, quite a pretty young girl appeared and invited us in. She was the daughter of the *gardien*, she told us. It was almost a shock to see something so fresh and young living in such a forbidding, torture-haunted den as Louis' Château of Loches. She was like one of the little bright-coloured winter blossoms springing out from a cranny of the grey walls. When she had lighted rather a smelly lantern, we prepared to follow into the "fastnesses" of the castle. If ever that good old double-dyed word could be appropriate, it is to Loches. I never thoroughly realised before the awful might of kings in feudal and mediæval days. To think that Louis XI. had the power to build such a place, and to hustle his enemies away for ever out of the sunshine, behind those tremendous walls, and bury them in the yard-square cells hollowed in the thickness of the stone! I used to wish I'd lived in those stirring times, but I changed my mind to-day —temporarily.

In the middle of the fortress is an enormous square, white keep, so heavy, solid, and imposing that it seems more like the slow work of Nature than of man. Down steep, winding steps in a tower, we followed our guide into the dungeons where that unspeakable Louis shut up the people he was afraid to leave in the world. Waving her lantern in the dusk, the girl showed us where the wretched prisoners had tried to keep themselves from madness by painting on the roof and walls. In one cell a bishop had cut into the solid wall a little altar, just where a slanting ray of sunshine stole through a grating and occasionally laid a small patch of light for a few minutes, only to snatch it away again. Several of the cells were just black holes scooped out of the rock, and there it seemed to have been Louis' delight to put some of the most important prisoners—men who had lived like princes, and had power over life and death in their own countries.

Oh, do you remember wily Cardinal Balue? I've

"AUNT MARY KODAKED ME."

been refreshing my memory of him in *Quentin Durward*, hating him dreadfully; but I did have a spasm of pity when I saw the big, well-like place where he was suspended for so many years, like an imprisoned canary, in a wooden cage, because he betrayed Louis' secrets to the Duke of Burgundy. Henry James says, in a fascinating Tauchnitz volume I bought in Tours (*A Little Tour in France*), that Cardinal Balue "survived much longer than might have been expected this extraordinary mixture of seclusion and exposure." Isn't that just the *cunningest* way of expressing it?

Last of all we went up to the top of a high tower in the midst of the Château, and there, as if we'd been on the mast-head of a ship, we had a bird's-eye view of the pretty white town, with the Indre murmuring by in sedgy meadows outside. There were some wonderful old cuttings in the stone, made by the soldiers who acted as sentinels and prisoners' guards; and Aunt Mary Kodaked me as I sat studying them. We could spy, across the plateau of the castle, the tomb of Agnes Sorel, and decided to go to it; but we left the poor girl till so late, finally, that we could only see her glimmering white in effigy of marble, with a sweetly resigned face, modest, folded hands, and a dear little soft sitting-down lamb to rest her pretty feet on. She had, besides, two very pretty young angels to watch over her and wake her up when it should be time.

I'm sure it would have taken at least three such angels to wake me up, until I had "slept out," after our long afternoon in the castle, and later in the town.

I went to bed early and slept ten hours. We hadn't to start immediately, as our drive for the day wasn't long, so I proposed to Aunt Mary that we should breakfast in our rooms and then go out for a morning walk. The breakfast idea appealed to her; not so the walk, and accordingly I had to go alone.   I had no plan except perhaps to buy a souvenir or two; but in the crooked street leading up to the castle I met Brown. He was reading a notice on the great gateway, directing strangers to some excavations lately made. He took off his cap at sight of me, and I asked him if he thought the excavations would be worth seeing. He had heard that they were, and I said that I should be glad if he would show me how to go to the place. I didn't like wandering about by myself. Everything is so horrid that one does by oneself in a strange country, and then if Brown isn't useful in one way he always proves to be in another. So he obeyed, of course, walking not too close, as if to let me see that he recognised the distance between us.   I've often noticed him do that if we have to go anywhere together on foot, and I think it's rather nice of him, don't you? Just a little pathetic too, maybe. Anyhow, it seems that way to me, for he really *ought* to have been a gentleman. It's such a waste of good material, the Lord using him up for a *chauffeur* when any common stuff would have done for that.

Well, we went on a short distance until we saw a tiny cottage in a wild-looking garden at the foot of the huge fortress walls. We rang a gate-bell, when another notice told us we'd got to the right place.

and a little, smiling woman came out to welcome us.
"Oh, yes!" said she volubly. She would show us
the excavations, and we would find them as interesting as anything we could see in Loches. Already it
was easy to see that in *her*, at least, we had found
something interesting. She had the nicest, brightest
old face, and she poured out upon us a kind of benign
dew of conversation. She introduced herself as
Madame César; always talking and explaining, she
lighted a candle, led us to the mouth of an egg-
shaped subterranean path, and bowed us down. She
went, too, down the steep steps, telling how this
passage and many ramifications of it had been discovered only recently, most of the excavations having
been the work of her husband. It was supposed that
an underground gallery led a long way from Loches
to some distant spot, so that people could come and
go to the castle unseen, and so that the fortress could
secretly receive provisions if it were besieged. All
sorts of things had been found in the passages—
rosaries, and old, old books, and coins, and queer
playing-cards; and some of the best of the relics
she had in her own cottage. We stopped to see
them afterwards, and she reeled forth yards of history
in the most fascinating and vivacious manner, accompanied by dramatic gestures, almost worthy of Sara
Bernhardt. I suppose she must have been down in
the excavations oftener than she could remember, but
you would have thought it was perfectly new to her,
and she was seeing it for the first time. She gave us
a rose each to remember her by, and oh!—wasn't it
comic, or tragic? which you will—she quite misunder-

stood things, and suggested that *I* should put Brown's rose in his leathery buttonhole.   He and I both pretended not to hear, but I felt embarrassed for a minute.   Nevertheless, I wouldn't have missed Madame César and her excavations for a good deal.

There, *déjeuner* is ready, and you'll be glad, maybe, dear, faraway Dad, because it will spare you further descriptions.   After *déjeuner* we shall proceed to be lightning-conducted again, and I shall duly collect a few more adventures to recount.   Good-bye, dear. How I wish you were with me instead of Aunt Mary!
                    Your everlasting
                                        Molly

JACK WINSTON TO LORD LANE

My dear Montie,

I have let you rest a good long time without
a letter (not that I've been taking a rest myself), and
now I should think you are opening your eyes with
astonishment at the picture on my paper of a hotel
at beautiful, blowy Biarritz. Thereby hangs a tale
of adventure and misadventure.

No doubt my fair employer believes me at this
moment to be consorting with couriers in the servants hall (if there be one) of her hotel. But, as
usual, I know a trick worth two of that; and having
washed his hands of Brown for the time being, your
friend Jack sits smoking his pipe and writing to you
in what is known as the "monkey-house" of this
hotel. As you don't know Biarritz, you'll think that
in exchanging all the comforts of a servants' hall for
a monkey-house I am not doing myself as well as
I might. But there are monkey-houses and monkey-
houses. This one is a delightful glass room built
on to the front of the hotel, facing a garden and
tennis courts, commanding a glorious view of the
sea and also of every creature, human and inhuman,
who goes by. One has tea in the monkey-house;

one writes letters, reads novels, smokes or gossips, according to sex and inclination; one can also be seen at one's private avocations by the madding crowd outside the glass house, hence the name.

The air is luminous with sunshine and pungent with ozone. Great green rollers are marching in, to break in thunder on the beach, and fling rainbow spouts of spray over tumbled brown rocks. In the distance the sea has all the colours of a peacock's tail; the world is at its best, and I ought to be rejoicing in its hospitality; but I'm not. The fact is, I'm upset in my mind. I'm over head and ears in love, and as there's no hope of scrambling out again (I'm hanged if I would, even if I could) or of getting my feet on solid ground, mere beauty of landscape and seascape appear slightly irrelevant.

I wouldn't bother you with my difficulties, which, I admit, are mostly my own fault, and serve me right for beginning wrong, but you asked in your letter if you could help me in any way; and it does help to let off steam. You are my safety-valve, old man.

You will have had my hasty line from Angoulême (birthplace of witch-stories and of Miss Randolph's beloved Francis the First) telling you how we got rid of Eyelashes. I don't think we shall ever encounter that beautiful young vision again, and I sincerely hope that we shall be spared others of his kind, but one never knows what will happen with an American girl at the helm. I told you also of our doings among the châteaux. Altogether, that was an idyllic time; and still, though I have been grumbling to you just now, when I can shut my eyes to to-morrow, I haven't much fault to find with Fate. You remember that weird story of Hawthorne's, about the man who walked out of his own house one morning, took lodgings in a neighbouring street, disguised himself, and watched for years the agony of his wife, who gave him up for dead? At last the desire for home came over him again; he knocked at his own door and went in; there the story ends.

My position is like that of Hawthorne's hero, without the tragedy. When shall I return to my own home? I cannot tell. I have stepped out of my own sphere into another, and sometimes I have an odd sense of detachment, as if I were floating in a void. It is only when I am writing to you or when I get letters from the world I have left that I feel the link which unites me with the past. Since I left Paris I have had only four letters from my world, which have fallen into Brown's world like strange reminders of another existence. I have had your own welcome words, and a letter from my mother at Cannes (I gave her my address at Poitiers) telling me of the arrival there of Jabez Barrow with his "one fair daughter," and urging me to haste. As if I should rush from the society of the Goddess in the car to the opulent charms (in both senses) of Miss Barrow! It appears that Jabez the Rich does not care for Cannes, but sighs for Italy, and that my mother has promised to "personally conduct" them to Rome. She wants me to reach Cannes before they leave, or if that's impossible, to abandon my car and follow by rail to Rome, lest I "miss this" great chance." I am not surprised at this move. My dear mother, when the travelling fit is upon her, is nothing if not erratic. She is here to-day, and, having seen the charms of another place advertised on a poster, is gone to-morrow.

On getting this letter a happy inspiration came into my mind. It had been the more or less vague intention of the Goddess, after inspecting the castles of the Loire, to steer for Lyons, arriving at Nice by way of Grenoble. I offered the wily suggestion, however, that it would make a more varied and less "obvious" tour if we went down by Bordeaux and Biarritz, snatched a glimpse of Spain, travelled along the foot of the Pyrenees to Marseilles, and so reach the Riviera by this long détour. The word "obvious" is a black beast to an American girl, who will be original or nothing; therefore my suggestion is in the way of being carried out. I've written to my mother that I can't reach Cannes before she herself leaves for Rome; thus I gain time. Still, the day of disclosure must come at last, and the longer it's put off the less I like to think about it.

The Goddess (alias Miss Randolph) is staying with her aunt at the "Angleterre." I have slunk off here, having arranged matters with the hall porter at the other place, who will, if my mistress wants me, send a messenger post-haste. Meanwhile the car reposes in a *garage*, where it is kept clean and in running order without any trouble to me. As I have gradually drifted into the position of Miss Randolph's courier as well as her *chauffeur*, I can plan these things as I like, for she never glances at her bills, which I settle, giving an account every few days. Do you recall your own story of the conscientious Yankee from the country who failed in his efforts to eat straight through the *menu* at a Paris hotel dinner, and appealed to the waiter to know whether he might now "skip from thar to thar"? Well, I would skip on my *menu* from Loches to Biarritz; but you were to have been my companion on this trip, and you cry for details.

From Loches we took a cross-country route which brought us out in the main road from Tours to Bordeaux at Dangé. There isn't much to say about that run, except that it was through agreeable, undulating country with wide horizons, like a thousand other undulations and horizons in France. At La Haye-Descartes we struck a pretty picture when crossing a bridge over the River Creuse. The setting sun had performed the miracle of turning the water into wine, and, chattering and laughing as if that wine had gone to their pretty heads, a company of girls and young women, all on their knees, cheerfully did their washing in the stream. It was one of those homely scenes that one is constantly coming across in this "pleasant land of France" to leave a picture in one's mind. Miss Randolph would have me stop the car on the bridge to watch it.

A queer thing about France, by the way. You and I have both been entertained right royally in jolly old *châteaux* by delightful French people of our own class. We know that life in such country houses can be as charming as it is in England; yet if one had never seen it from the inside, one would fancy in

travelling that nothing of the sort existed.　**Roughly,**
one might sum the difference up in a phrase by
saying that France presents a peasant's landscape,
England a landlord's.　In England you see twenty
good country houses for every one you pass in France
—excepting only the district of the Loire; and
outdoor life as we know it, on the road and on the
river, doesn't seem to exist over here.　Somehow
I was never so much struck with this contrast before,
though I know this country almost as well as I know
my hat.　Think of the English roads and lanes, of
the pretty girls and decent men one meets on horse-
back or in smart dogcarts, the dowagers in victorias,
the crowds of cyclists, the occasional fine motor-car,
knickerbockered men walking for the pleasure of
exercise!　Here, though one knows there are more
motors than at home, one rarely comes across them
out of towns; and as for ladies and gentlemen, or,
indeed, any sort of people out solely for enjoyment,
they're as rare as black opals.　I look in vain for
pretty field paths and rural lanes, where workmen
and their sweethearts wander when the day is done.
I suppose they prefer to do their love-making indoors
or in front of a café, or perhaps they sandwich it in
with their long hours of work, and that is the reason
why the whole of France seems so much more cultivated than country England—the reason why
every acre is turned to account, not a square yard
of earth left untilled.　It's only the magnificent roads
which aren't enough appreciated, apparently, by the
"nobility and gentry," as the tradesmen's circulars
have it.　And what roads the Routes Nationales are

—born for motor-cars!—varying a little from department to department, but equally good almost everywhere. You come to a stone marking the boundary of a department, for instance, and crossing an imaginary line, find yourself on a different kind of surface, each department being allowed to make it's road after the manner which pleases it best—provided only it makes it well.

The Route Nationale from Paris to Bayonne, along part of which we've lately travelled, is good nearly all the way. From Dangé to Poitiers is a splendid bit, and up to Poitiers one climbs a considerable hill. It's a cheerful town, with a fine cathedral, and lively streets full of red-legged soldiers, rather weedy and shambling fellows, like most French conscripts. Beyond Poitiers the road is one long, exhilarating switchback—you rush down one hill, climb another, swoop again into a hollow, and so on, the road unrolling itself like a great white tape. You try to drive faster than the tape unrolls, but somehow you can never beat it.

That we were getting into the south was shown by the fact that the road was bordered by endless rows of walnut trees. Under a tumbled sky, and with an occasional spatter of rain, we passed that day through a vast stretch of rolling, cultivated land, with obscure villages at long intervals. In a little town called Couhé-Verac we lunched rather late. The regular *déjeuner* was over, as it was nearly three in the afternoon; but in ten minutes after we got into the house we sat down to this luncheon: boiled eggs, roast veal, *bœuf à la mode*, *purée* of potatoes, pheasant, a delicious *pâté*, grapes, peaches, pears, sweet biscuits, cream cheese, red and white wine, and bread *ad libitum;* all for two francs fifty per head. Think of it! This was a homely village inn, with no pretensions. What would have happened if we had turned up unexpectedly at such a house in England? We should have been offered cold beef and pickles, with the alternative of ham and eggs, or possibly "chop or steak, sir; take twenty minutes." Truly in cooking we are barbarians. The French dine; we feed.

The landlord was a man of character. He had delightful manners, and though he was young his hair was greyish, and cut low and straight across a broad forehead. Through gold-rimmed glasses gleamed the blue eyes of an enthusiast. He went with me to look at the car, and explained that he was an inventor—that he had designed a new system of marine propulsion more powerful than the screw. It followed the action of a man in swimming, "regular in irregularity," and standing on his toes, he flung out his arms, and beat them rhythmically in the air to illustrate his theory. It was hard, he confided in me, to have to keep an inn in a small town, when he ought to be in Paris, among engineers, perfecting his invention. Did I, by any chance, know of a capitalist who would back him? I sympathised and regretted; but who knows if he has not got hold of an idea? At Blois they have a statue of Denis Papin, who, the French say, invented the steam engine. Perhaps, years hence, if my grandchildren pass through Couhé-Verac, they may see a statue to the blue-eyed landlord of its little inn.

Beyond Couhé-Verac we had our first dog accident. Dogs, you know, are as great a nuisance to automobiles as they are to cycles, and they charge at one's car with such vehemence that their impetus almost carries them under the wheels. Sometimes they show their strength by galloping alongside the car for a couple of hundred yards, barking so furiously the while that their bodies are contorted by the violence of the effort. I was driving at a moderate pace (something under thirty miles an hour) when a beautiful collie which had been standing by the roadside walked quietly out and planted himself with his back to me in front of the car. The fact was that he saw his master coming along the road, and had gone forward to greet him. The whole thing happened in an instant, so that I had no time to stop. I think the dog must have been deaf not to hear the noise of the car. I shouted, but he took no notice. To swerve violently to one side was to risk upsetting the car; besides, there was no room to do this as another vehicle happened to be passing. If there had been only the car to sacrifice, I would have sacrificed it to save that collie; but I couldn't sacrifice Miss Randolph. There was nothing for it but to drive over the dog. With a sickening wrench of the heart, I saw the nice beast disappear under the front of the car. Instantly slowing down, I looked behind me expecting to see a mangled corpse. But there was the dog rolling over and over on the road. Clearly some under part of the car had struck him and sent him spinning. The noise, the unexpected blow, the fierce, hot blast of the poisonous exhaust

pouring into his face, must have made the poor
fellow think that he had struck a travelling earth-
quake. But happily he was unhurt. As I looked
he got on to his feet, and with his tail between his
legs, ran to his master for consolation. Our last
glimpse showed us that comedy had followed tragedy,
for the master was beating the dog with a cane for
getting in our way. I was afraid Miss Randolph
would scream or faint, but she did neither, only
turned white as marble, and never looked prettier in
her life. Aunt Mary yelled, of course, but more in
fear for ourselves than for the collie, I think. She
says she would like dogs better "if their bark could
be extracted."

Angoulême is, like Poitiers, a town set upon a hill,
a quaint old town, worth seeing, but we were eager
now to get to the true South, and merely gave ourselves time to lunch (the waiter producing, with a
flourish, enticing but indigestible *pâtés de perdrix aux
truffes*) and to drive slowly along some of the famous
terraced boulevards that form the distinction and the
charm of Angoulême. Certainly the place stands
romantically on its high and lonely hill, almost sur-
rounded by the clear waters of the Charante. At
Angoulême we saw, I may say, the first professional
beggars we had met on the tour. A warm sun seems
to breed beggars as it breeds mosquitoes, or is it that
Southern peoples have less self-respect than the
Northern?

A drawback to automobilism in France is the fact
that many of the great direct main roads are *pavé*.
I believe that this is a remnant of the old days of

road-making, when these heavy cobbles formed the one surface that would stand artillery. For ordinary traffic the *pavé* roads are impossible, and their existence must be a drawback to trade and intercourse. In France they sell special bicycling maps showing with dotted lines all the *pavé* roads, and these I have carefully studied, as it is worth making any *détour* to avoid the awful jolting of the *pavé*. But somehow, bewteen Angoulême and Bordeaux, I took a wrong turning, and suddenly on ahead of us the good road ceased abruptly as if a straight line had been ruled across it, and the detestable *pavé* began.

"Oh, let's try it as an experience," commanded my Goddess. "I hate going back, and perhaps it doesn't last long." I trusted to this hope, for I knew that in many places the *pavé* is being dug up, here and there only short stretches of it being left, and I gingerly drove the Napier on to the execrable surface of uneven stones. We rattled and tossed, and steering became a matter of difficulty. The irritating thing was that each side of this detestable road were wide belts of inviting grass, but with malignant ingenuity these are cut up at frequent intervals by oblique drainage gutters, which forbid the passage of anything wider than a bicycle. For bicycles there are indeed special tracks kept in order by the Touring Club de France, but all four-wheeled vehicles must jolt and bump along the rough, uneven stones. By the time we reached the first cross-road Aunt Mary begged for mercy, and I was glad to have the order to get off the *pavé* at any cost. Soundly as the Napier is built, it was a tremendous and unfair strain upon springs and tyres, and all the while I was dreading that something would go. Threading our way through endless vineyards by a labyrinth of by-ways, we ran through Barbezieux and Libourne, and as day was falling crossed the noble bridge over the Garonne into bustling Bordeaux.

Next day we took a run on the car along the Quai des Chartrons and through some of the chief streets and squares of Bordeaux, just to get a glimpse of the handsome town, at which Miss Randolph turned up her pretty nose because it was "new and prosperous"; then, guided by a porter from the hotel who went before us on his bicycle, we threaded the city on our way out to Arcachon. There was some unavoidable *pavé* and many odious tramlines; but at last our guide left us on the outskirts of the town, and we sped on to a curious little toy suburb called St. Martin, studded with neat, one-storied, red-roofed cottages, like houses in a child's box of bricks, and all with romantic names, such as Belle Idée, Mon Repos, Augustine, Mon Cœur, and so on The whole place seemed like an assemblage of dove cotes specially planned for honeymoon couples, and gave the oddest effect of unreality. Then we passed into the green twilight of the great pine forest which extends all the way to the sea.

A romantically beautiful road lay before us. For more than thirty miles it runs straight and smooth through high aromatic pines, springing from a carpet of bracken. Miss Randolph, I must tell you, has become an expert driver, and at sight of the long, straight road said she would take the wheel. So I stopped a moment, and we changed places. She put the car at its highest speed, and we flew along the infinite perspective of the never-ending avenue. This vast pine forest is a desert, and we passed only through small and scattered villages. That flight through the pine forest of the Landes will always be to me an ineffaceable memory. None of us spoke; two of us felt, I think, that we were close to Nature's heart. The heady, balsamic odour of the pines exhilarated us, and the wind, playing melancholy music on the Eolian harps of their branches, seemed like a deep accompaniment to the humming throb of the tireless motor. As often as I dared I stole a look sideways at Miss Randolph's profile. She sat erect, her little gauntletted hands resting light as thistledown upon the wheel, but her fingers and her wrist nervous and alert as a jockey riding a thoroughbred, her eyes intent on the long, straight road before her, and a look almost of rapture upon her face.

We had raced silently through the forest for nearly an hour, when, mingling with the balsam of the pines there came a pungent odour of ozone floating from open blue spaces beyond the sombre girdle of the pines. Miss Randolph threw at me a questioning glance. "It must be the sea," I answered, and in a few moments more, after passing through the ancient town of La Teste, we came out upon the edge of a vast lagoon, semicircular, the distant shores almost lost in an indistinct blue haze. "The Bassin d'Arcachon. I said" Still, no town was visible, only the great expanse of landlocked sea, its shore dotted with the brown wooden cabins of the oyster fishers. It seemed like coming to the end of the world.

Slowing down a little, we followed a raised causeway that skirted the edge of the Bassin, and presently entered upon a long, straight street—one of the oddest streets you have ever seen, one whole side of it (that next the sea) being composed of fantastic bungalows and pleasure-houses of all imaginable styles, each set in its own garden, and the whole town drowned in an ocean of pines. At the outskirts I took the helm again, for Miss Randolph scarcely trusts her skill in traffic. Not that there was enough to be alarming in Arcachon, for the place seemed under a spell of silence. We drove through the long main street, past an imposing white château and a good many quite charming houses, until we came to a hotel which the Goddess fancied, and turned into a garden. I'd never been to Arcachon before, and supposed from the guidebooks that this was the place for "my ladies" (as the couriers say) to stop. But the landlady came out, and welcoming us with one breath, recommended us with the next to their winter house in the forest. This place, looking over the sea, was for summer; the other was now more agreeably sheltered.

The "house in the forest" sounded well in the ears of the Goddess, so we drove off to find it, according to the directions of Madame Feras. The Napier spun us up a steep, winding road into a charming garden surrounding an Alhambra sort of place, which Aunt Mary thought "real gay," being bitterly disappointed to find it was not our hotel, but Arcachon's casino. The garden proved to be, however, practically the beginning of the *Ville d'Hiver*, a quaint and delightful collection of villas which look as if they had been scattered like ornate seeds among the crowding pine of the Landes. Of these seeds the "Continental" is the most imposing, and, by-the-way, this climate would suit you, I should think; it's an extraordinary combination of pine and sea air, which would make a doctor's fortune as a tonic, if he could cork it up in bottles.

As both hotels are run by the same management, I feared gossip if I went down to the "Grand" and did the Doctor Jekyll act; so I cautiously remained Mr. Hyde, alias Brown, and was a serf among other serfs. After dining in the society of maids and valets (whose manners and conversation would have given me ripping "copy" if I were a journalist) I stole out to cleanse my mind with a draught of pure air and a look at the sky. A cat may look at a king, and a *chauffeur* may walk on a terrace built for his betters, especially if the betters elect to shut themselves up in stuffy drawing-rooms, with every window anxiously closed. I availed myself of this privilege, for the hotel has a fine terrace. As it was apparently empty, I sauntered along with my nose in the air and my eyes on the stars, letting my footsteps take care of themselves. Suddenly there was a startled "Oh!" in a familiar voice, and I became aware that I had collided with the Goddess, who had also been thinking of the stars and not of her feet—which, by-the-by, *I* very often think of, as they are the prettiest I ever saw.

I instantly clapped my pipe in my pocket, where it revenged itself on me for neglecting to put it out by burning a hole through to my skin. I apologised, and would have taken my humble chauffeury self away, but my mistress detained me. "What is that wonderful, faraway sound, Brown?" she asked in the delicious way she has of expecting me to know everything, as if I were an encyclopædia and she'd only to turn over my leaves to come to a new fact.

I stopped breathing to listen; I'd do it permanently to please her. And there *was* a sound— a wonderful sound. If I hadn't been thinking about her and the stars, I should have been conscious of it before. Out of the night-silence the sound seemed to grow, and yet be a part of the silence, or rather, to intensify the *near* silence by its distant booming, deep and ominous, like the far-off roaring of angry lions never pacified. At first I thought it must be a rush of wind surging through the mighty pine forest; but not a dark branch moved against the spangled embroidery of stars, though the air seemed faintly to vibrate with the continuous, solemn note. Suddenly the meaning of the sound came to me; it was the majestic music of the Atlantic surf beating on the bar ten miles away. But it was too divine standing there in the night with Her in silence. For a moment I had not the heart to speak and tell her of my discovery. A faint light came to us from the stars and from the curtained windows of the hotel. I could just see her face and her lovely great eyes looking up questioningly in absolute confidence at me. Jove, what wouldn't I have given just then

"DARK-FACED PEASANTS PERCHED ON STILTS."

to be Jack Winston and not Brown! If I had been, that girl wouldn't have got back into the house without being proposed to, and having another "scalp" to count, as they say American beauties do. Not that I think she'd be that kind. I don't know how long I shouldn't have tried to make the magic of the moment last, if Aunt Mary hadn't bounced out of the hotel (done up in a shawl, like a large parcel) to call "Molly! Molly, it's time you came in!"

Molly didn't move, but Aunt Mary descended the steps, relentless as fate; so I made the most of my information, and added a short disquisition on Arcachon oysters and oyster fishing, for the sake of retaining the Goddess's society. Unfortunately, however, I happened to remark that the oyster women wore trousers exactly like the men, and this so disgusted Miss Kedison that she incontinently dragged her niece from the contamination of the *chauffeur's* presence.

Next day was Sunday. Miss Randolph went to the English church, which is the prettiest I've ever seen in France, and afterwards, escorted by the chaplain with whom she'd made friends, went forth to see the sights, while I inquired as to how we might best proceed upon our way. While Miss Randolph and Miss Kedison read their prayer-books, I studied that useful volume, *Les Routes de France*, and was duly warned against the impracticable roads of the Landes. The one thing to do, according to the oracle, was to return to Bordeaux and make a long détour to Bayonne by Mont de Marsan. I knew Miss Randolph would dislike this plan, for she hates

going back, and so do I.   If I had been alone, or
with you, I would have chanced it without a
moment's hesitation, making straight for Bayonne
by way of the forbidden Landes, with all its pitfalls.
But I funked the idea of perhaps getting Her into
a mess—and hearing Aunt Mary say "I told you
so," as she invariably does when there's any trouble.

To my joy, however, plucky Parson Radcliff had
actually advanced the idea of the Landes, during
their excursion, and the Goddess sent for me on
Sunday evening, full of enthusiasm. Far be it from
me to dampen the ardour of youth; and early on
Monday morning we started to follow the route
La Teste, Sanguinet, Parentis, Yehoux, Liposthey,
which names reminded Miss Randolph of *Gulliver's
Travels*.

She and I were in fine spirits, expecting the unexpected, and bracing ourselves to encounter difficulties. There was mystery in the very thought
of the Landes—that strange waste of forest and
sand so little known outside its own people. I felt
it, and so did Miss Randolph, I knew. How I knew
I couldn't explain to you; but some electric current
usually communicates her mood to me, and I should
almost believe from various signs that it was so with
her in regard to me, if I weren't a mere *chauffeur* in
the lady's pay.

For some distance the going was good, but we
were only reading the preface to the true Landes as
yet; and when we reached the boundary post between
the department of the Gironde and the real Landes,
there was one of those sudden, complete changes

I've mentioned in the quality of the road. To drive into this dim, pine-clad region was like driving back into the years a century or two. A motor-car was an anachronism, and if we came to grief our blood was upon our own heads. The way became grass-grown and rutty, and I was obliged to drive slowly. Deeper and deeper we penetrated into the forest, and deeper and deeper also we sank into the soft earth. Aunt Mary groaned and prophesied disaster as we crawled along in ruts up to our axles; but I think Miss Randolph and I would have perished sooner than retreat. I trusted in the Napier and she trusted in me. In one place the road had been mended with a covering of loose rocks rather than stones; we panted and crunched our way over them, enormously to the astonishment of the road-menders and one or two dark-faced peasants, perched like cranes on the old-fashioned stilts not yet utterly abandoned as a means of navigating this sea of sand and pines. Still, on we went, the engine labouring a little, like an over-worked heart; but it was a loyal heart, and the tyres were trumps.

Miss Randolph said that if she were a tyre and condemned to such hard labour, she would burst out of sheer spite. I think Miss Kedison nearly did so as it was; but as for us (I suppose you can't conceive the satisfaction to a poor *chauffeur* of bracketing his lady and himself familiarly as "us"), we were intoxicated by the heavy balsam of the turpentine, for which every tree we passed was being sliced. On each a great flake of the trunk had been struck off with an axe, and a small earthen cup affixed to catch the resin, which is the heart's blood of the wounded tree. There was something Dante-esque in the effect of these bleeding wounds, among old, scarcely healed scars; and that effect was intensified by the shadowy gloom of the dense forest, and the never-ceasing sound of the wind among the high, dark branches, like the beating of surf upon an unseen shore.

At last, when the feeling was strong upon us that the ocean of pines had engulphed us, like Pharaoh's chariot in the Red Sea, we came upon a rambling village, called Parentis. As if to announce the arrival of the first motor car ever seen in the dim, forgotten Landes, the off front tire began to hiss. "I *told* you so!" said Aunt Mary. My eyes and Miss Randolph's met, and we both burst out laughing. It was a great liberty in me, and though I couldn't have helped it to save my neck, and became preternaturally solemn afterwards as a penance, I don't believe that the lady I should like to have for an aunt-in-law will ever forgive me. She ought, however, as this was our first accident with the Napier, while with poor little Miss Randolph's late esteemed Dragon, one breakfasted, lunched, dined, and supped on horrors. Besides, the Dragon invariably schemed to do its worst, far from human aid, while my long-suffering Napier had brought us to the very courtyard of the village inn before (as Miss Randolph expressed it) "sitting down to rest."

Inside this convenient courtyard I set about doing the repairs, jacking up the car, taking off the tyre, patching it, and getting it on again in twenty minutes;

not bad for an amateur *mécanicien*. All the people
of the inn and many of the villagers gathered round
to see the great sight, and Aunt Mary consoled herself by showing off her somewhat eccentric French
to the landlady and her family.

There were three generations in this group, I took
time to notice. A bowed and wrinkled old dame;
her daughter, a strong, sad-faced woman in black;
and a golden-haired granddaughter, about the prettiest creature I ever saw — bar one. And it was
charming to see my Goddess laying herself out to
be nice to the trio. Her personality (which is the
last word in well-groomed, high-strung, vivacious
American girlhood) contrasted strikingly with these
countrywomen, who had perhaps never been outside their own forest. I couldn't hear what she was
saying, but she has the most extraordinary way of
always hitting on the right thing to please and
interest people, without departing from truth or
descending to flattery. All three gazed at her with
delight and admiration, the little beauty of the
Landes with deepening colour and wistful eyes.
No Frenchwoman, no Englishwoman, no woman
save an American of the best type, could have exactly that manner, which is indescribable to one
who doesn't know. Strange for a vision like that
to flash into these quiet lives, then flash away, never
to be seen again—only remembered.

It was too early for luncheon, but as we had had
the shelter of the inn I wanted to order something
for "the good of the house." I accordingly asked
for Bordeaux and biscuits, and the pretty rose of a

granddaughter brought a bottle of—what do you think? Pontet Canet! It was nectar, and cost—three francs a bottle !

When we drove away Miss Randolph was reflective. I would have liked to offer a penny for her thoughts, but that sort of indulgence is not in the sphere of a *chauffeur*. Presently she broke out, however. "Did you ever see anything so lovely as that girl?" she exclaimed. "She's all white and gold and rose. Her presence in that sombre place reminds me of a shaft of warm, golden light breaking through the dark canopy of pines. She's like a maiden in Hans Christian Andersen. And her name's Angèle. Isn't that perfect? It seems cruel that such a creature, who would make a sensation in Paris or London or New York, must bloom and ripen and wither at last, unknown, in that wilderness. Oh, how I should love to snatch her away?"

"What would you do with her, miss, if you could?" I ventured to ask, at my humblest—which in Aunt Mary's eyes, is my best. "Would you take her for your maid?"

"A *maid?*" echoed my Goddess scornfully. "Why, if I meant such a crime as that, I should expect white bears to come out of these woods and devour me. No; I would give her pretty dresses, and arrange a good marriage for her."

"Is that what young girls in America like, miss," I meekly inquired, "to have marriages arranged for them?"

"No; they hate it, and go away from America to show that they hate it—sometimes; but this would

be different," said she. And I wondered if she had
accidentally betrayed anything.

At Liposthey we struck the direct road, with
good surface, from Bordeaux to Bayonne. Thus on
through Labouheyre to Castets, still walled in with
dark, balsamic forest, where we lunched. Just beyond, however, we found that we were bidding the
pines farewell, and we were regretting them despite
the beauty of the road—increasing every moment—
when suddenly we had a great surprise. At what
precise point it came I don't quite know, for I was
snatched up out of the dull "flatland" of facts. Miss
Randolph was driving, and I was glancing interestedly
about, as an intelligent young man of the working-
class may, when away to the left I saw up in the
skies a long chain of blue, serrated mountains looking far too high to belong to this world. I started
on my seat; then Miss Randolph saw what I saw.
"Oh—h!" she breathed, with a responsive sigh of
appreciation. Not an adjective; not a word. I
blessed her for that. Unfortunately, Aunt Mary
seized this moment to awake, and she did not spare
us fireworks. She never does. She is one of those
women who insist upon your knowing that they have
a soul for beauty. But she went to sleep again when
she had used up all her rockets, and left the Goddess
and me alone with the Pyrenees. Much nearer
Bayonne we had another surprise—a notice, in
English, by the roadside: "To the Guards' Ceme-
tery." An odd sign to come across in France, *n'est
ce pas, mon brave?* And just as I was calling up the
past, Miss Randolph exclaimed: "I wonder if *your*

Napier is any relation to *that* Napier?" which shows that she has the Peninsular Campaign at her finger-ends; or else Aunt Mary has been cramming her out of a guide-book.

It was not late in the afternoon when we crossed the bridge over the Adour (*she* says the proverb, "Don't cross your bridges till you get to them," can't apply to France, as you're always getting to them), but already the sky was burnished with sunset; and if there's anything finer than a grand and ancient fortified gateway turned to copper by the sun, I don't know it. I advised Miss Randolph to come back one day from Biarritz, if we stayed long enough, to see the exquisite old glass window for which the Bayonne cathedral is famous; but it was too late to pause for such details as windows then, so we flew on along the switchback road over the remaining five miles to Biarritz. Here, in this agreeable town, we play about till I have orders from headquarters to proceed. Our programme is now to go straight along the Pyrenees to Marseilles, and so to Nice. Ah, if only I can get Her to go on to Italy! You had better address me next at the Riviera Palace, Cimiez. We are to pause at Pau, call at Carcassonne, and honour other places *en route* to the Riviera, so there ought to be ample time for this long screed to reach you and for you to send reproach or praise to Nice. Tell me about yourself; how you are; what you read; what girl you love.

Your sincere, but somewhat selfish friend,

JACK WINSTON.

MOLLY RANDOLPH TO HER FATHER

HOTEL GASSION, PAU,
December 14.

Dear Universal Provider of Love and Cheques,

Thank you a thousand times for both, which have just been forwarded along the route of this "wild-goose chase," as you call it. Well, if it is one, I don't know who the goose is, unless Aunt Mary. She is rather like that sometimes, poor dear; but we get on splendidly. Oh, I would get on splendidly with five Aunt Marys (which Heaven forbid!), for I'm *so* happy, Dad! I'm having such a good time— *the* time of my life, or it would be if you were in it.

If you ever lose all your money and come a nice, gentlemanly cropper in the street called Wall, we might come to Biarritz to live, just you and I. We *would* have fun! And we could stop in our pretty little cheap villa all the year round, for one season only waits politely till another is out to step in; it's always gay and fashionable, and yet you needn't be either unless you like. And the sea and sky have more gorgeous colour in them than any other sea and sky, and the air has more ozone; and the brown rocks that go running a hippopotamus race out into the beryl-green water are queerer and finer

149

than any other rocks. So you see everything is superlative, even the hotels, and *as* for a certain Confectioner; but he, or rather she, deserves a capital. There are drives and walks, and curio-shops where I spent my little all; and there's fox-hunting, which would be nice if it weren't for the poor tame fox; and golf, and *petits cheveaux* at the casino, where Aunt Mary gambled before she knew what she was doing, and kept on a long time after she did; and mysterious Basque persons with an-cestors and costumes more wonderful than anybody else's, who dance strange dances in the streets for money, and play a game called La Pelotte, which is great sport to watch. And you walk by the sea, with its *real* waves, like ours at home, not little tuppenny-ha'penny ones like those I saw in the English Channel; and you look across an opal bay through a creamy haze to a mystic land made entirely of tumbled blue mountains. And then, one of the best things about Biarritz is that you're next door to Spain. Ah, that door of Spain! I've knocked and been in through it, but just across the threshold. The way of it was like this—

I'd been up early and out to the golf course for a lesson from the professional; when I came home a little before eleven Brown was waiting. He wanted to know if I wouldn't care to have a peep at Spain, and said that we could easily go there and back by dinner-time. Aunt Mary and I were ready in a "jiffy," so was the car, and we were buzzing away along a beautiful road (though a little "*accidentée*," as the French say) near the ocean. There were the most lovely lights I ever saw on land or sea, over the mountains and the great, unquiet Atlantic; and St. Jean de Luz, which we came to in no time, as it seemed, was another charming little watering-place for us to come and live if you get poor. A good many English people do live there all the year round, and whom do you think is one of them? George Gissing. You know how I made you read his books, and you said they seemed so real that you felt you had got into the people's houses by mistake, and ought to say "Excuse me"? Well, he has come to live in St. Jean de Luz, the all-knowing Brown tells me. His master admires Mr. Gissing very much, so the Honourable John must be a nice and clever man.

As for history, Brown is an inexhaustible mine. I simply "put in my thumb and pull out a plum." But I forgot—there *aren't* usually plums in mines, are there, except in the prospectuses? Anyhow, it was Brown who made me realise what tremendously interesting things *frontiers* are. That imaginary line, and then—people, language, costumes, and customs changing as if a fairy had waved a wand. The frontier between France and Spain is a great wide river—on purpose to give us another bridge. Doesn't the name, "Bidassoa," suggest a broad, flowing current running swiftly to the sea?

This time we would have none of the bridge. It was too much bother paying duty on the car, and having a lot of red tape about getting it back again in an hour or two; so we left Balzac, as I have named it, at the last French town and rowed across.

on past the first Spanish town, Irun, to a much older, more picturesque one—Fuenterrabia. A particularly handsome boatman wanted to row us, but Brown would do it himself, either to show how well he can manage the oars, or else because the boatman had abnormally long eyelashes, and Brown is rather sick of eyelashes.

Even crossing the river and going down towards the mouth of the stream (with a huge, old ruined castle towering up to mark Fuenterrabia) was quite thrilling, because of the things in history that have happened all around. The estuary runs down to the sea between mountains of wild and awesome shapes. One of them is named after Wellington, because it is supposed to look like his profile lying down, and the other mountains had a chance to see his real profile many times, though I'll be bound his enemies never saw his back. He fought among them—both mountains and enemies, and the latter were some of Napoleon's smartest marshals. He took a whole army across the ford in the Bidassoa, attacked Soult, and chased him all the way up the mountains to the very summit of La Rhune, a great conical peak high up in the sky. Another thing was the Isle des Faisans, right in the middle of the river, where Philippe and Louis the Fourteenth fixed everything up about Louis' Spanish bride. It's the smallest island you ever saw; you wouldn't think there would be room for a whole King of Spain and a King of France to stand on it at the same time, much less sign contracts.

When our boat touched Spanish soil on the beach

below Fuenterrabia, two rather ferocious-looking Spaniards in uncomfortable uniforms were waiting for us. They had the air of demanding "your money or your life"; but after all it was only the extraordinarily high, ugly collars of their overcoats which gave them such a formidable appearance. They were custom-house officers guarding the coast, though how they see over those collars to find out what's going on under their noses I don't know. Brown says that soldiers at Madrid have to dress like that in winter to protect themselves from the terrible icy winds, and as Madrid sets the fashion for everything in Spain, the provincial soldiers have to choke themselves in the same way.

It did seem to me that the very air of Spain was different from across the river in France. It was richer and heavier, like incense. It *is* nice to have an imagination, isn't it, instead of having to potter about leading *facts* by a string, as if they were dogs? Well, anyway, I am sure people have bigger and blacker eyes in Spain. Just walking up from the beach to the strange old town, I saw two or three peasant women and children with wonderful eyes, like black velvet with stars shining through—eyes that princesses would give fortunes for.

I couldn't help humming "In Old Madrid" under my breath, and I fancied that the salt-smelling breeze brought the snapping of castanets. The sun was hot; but coolness, and rich, tawny shadows swallowed us up in a silent street, crowded with fantastic, beautifully carved, bright-coloured houses, all having balconies, each one more overhanging than the other. Not a soul was to be seen; our footsteps rang on the narrow side-walk, and it seemed rude of our voices when we talked to wake the sleepy silence out of its afternoon nap. But suddenly a handsome young man appeared from a side street, and stopping in the middle of the road, vigorously tinkled a musical bell. Immediately the street became alive. Each house door showed a man; women hung over the gaily-draped balconies; children ran out and clustered round the bell-ringer. He began to speak very fast in guttural Spanish, and we couldn't understand a word he said, though Brown has a smattering of the language—enough to get on with in shops and hotels. When he had finished everyone laughed. All up and down the street came the sound of laughter; deep, bass laughter from the men; contralto laughter from the women. The handsome bell-ringer laughed too, and then vanished as suddenly as he had come. All the life of the quaint street seemed to fade away with him. Slowly the people took themselves indoors; the balconies were empty; the street silent as in a city of the dead. It was like something on the stage; but I suppose it's just a bit of everyday life in Fuenterrabia and old, old Spain.

We went on up to the castle we had seen from the beach, and I turned my eyes away from a big, ugly round building, like a country panorama-place, for that was the bull ring, and the one thing that makes Spain hateful to me. I didn't want even to think of it. The gateway of the palace—for it had been a palace—was splendid—an arch across the street. But on the other side I burst out laughing at a sign, in what was meant to be English, advertising the castle for sale. Capitals were sprinkled about everywhere; the painter had thought they would look pretty, and evidently it was held out as a lure to Britishers and Americans that Charles the Fifth had built it and lived in it. I know Mrs. Washington Potts would love to buy it, and then go home and mention in an absent-minded manner that she'd "acquired a royal palace in Spain as a winter residence." Can't you hear her? But oh, poor palace! It's as airy a mansion now as most castles in Spain, though what's left of its walls is about fifteen feet thick. Still, the glorious view of sea and mountains from the roof would be worth paying for, and wouldn't need thousands of dollars' worth of restoration, like the house.

While we lingered in Fuenterrabia absorbing the atmosphere of old Spain, the time was inconsiderate enough to run away and leave us with only a twisted channel among sandbanks to remember it by. So we took an oddly shaped carriage with a white tasselled awning on it and drove back to Hendaye and our motor-car. But the day was a great success, and I congratulated Brown, which Aunt Mary said it was silly to do, as it is his business to think of everything for us.

Now, as you see by the date of my letter, we're at Pau, to which we came from Biarritz in a delicious morning's run through a pearl-coloured landscape trimmed with blue mountains. As we got into the town the Lightning Conductor, who was driving, whisked us through a few streets, swooped round a large square, and suddenly stopped the car on a broad terrace with an air as though he said, "There! what do you think of *that?*" I think I gasped. I know I wanted to by way of saluting what must be one of the most wonderful views in the whole world.

We had stopped on a terrace not the least like a street. At one end was an old grey château; then a long line of imposing buildings, almost too graceful to be hotels, which they really were; a church sending a white, soaring spire into the blue sky; an open, shady *place*, with a statue of Henri Quatre; villas hotels, hotels villas in a sparkling line, with great trees to cut it and throw a blue haze of shadow. That is one side of the terrace. The other is an iron railing, a sudden drop into space, and—the view. Your eyes travel across a park where even in this mid-winter season roses are blooming and date palms are flourishing. Then comes a hurrying river, giving life and music to the landscape; beyond that a wide sweep of hills, with bunches of poplars, and valleys where white villages lie half concealed; and further still, leaping into the sky, the immense line of the Pyrenees, looking to-day so near and sharply out-lined that they seemed to be cut out of cardboard. When I was able to speak I told Brown that the very first thing I should do would be to walk to those delectable mountains. "I don't think you could quite manage it, miss," he said, with his quiet smile, "for they are nearly forty miles away." Then we turned round and drove into the courtyard of the hotel, which faces the great view.

It looked tremendously swell, and Aunt Mary and I tried to live up to it by sweeping haughtily in as if we hadn't collected any of the historic dust of France on our motoring coats and hats. Just as we were acquitting ourselves quite creditably who should step out from a group of the very people we were hoping to impress with our superiority but Jimmy Payne! Oh, you wicked old man, I believe you must have wired or written him a hint. You know you have a weakness for Jimmy, or rather for his family. But I can't go about marrying the sons of all the pretty ladies you were in love with in your vanished youth. Probably there were dozens, for you're as soft-hearted as you are hard-headed, and you can't deny it.

Still, I don't mind confessing that I was rather pleased to see Jimmy, not a bit because he is *Jimmy*, but because he seemed to bring a breath of homey-ness with him, and it is nice to have an old friend turn up in a "far countree" when you've got dust on your hat and the other women who are staring at you haven't. If only the friend doesn't proceed to bore you by insisting on being something more than a friend, which I hope Jimmy is by this time tired of doing, I think I shall rather enjoy the encounter than otherwise. As for anything else, it doesn't appeal to *me* that he's his mother's son, or that he's clever in stocks, or that he's got as much money as you have. So now you know, and I hope he does.

Well, we talked a little, and then I found that Aunt Mary was chattering like mad with the Garrisons (one "talks" oneself; other people "chatter"; foreigners "jabber"; so we were all glad to see each other, or said so, which comes to the same thing.

"How's your automobile?" was almost the first thing I asked Jimmy, for the last time I'd seen him it was the pride of his heart. "I suppose," I said, "that, like us, you're making a tour around Europe on it?"

I thought his face changed a little, though I don't know why it should. "Oh," said he, "I've lent it to my friend Lord Lane; charming fellow I met last year in Paris. He'll meet me with it a little later. Where are *you* going after this?"

"We're working slowly on to the Riviera," said I.

"Oh, isn't that funny," said Jimmy, "that's where Lord Lane and I are going to meet! At Cannes, or Nice, or Monte Carlo; it isn't quite settled yet which. I suppose you're going to all of them, as you're driving about on a car?"

I said that we expected to, and pointed through the glass door at my automobile, with Brown superintending the hotel servants who were lifting down the luggage. He looked hard at the car and the *chauffeur*, as if he envied me both, and I think he had something more to say which he considered important, but I was in a hurry to change and make myself prettier—*much* prettier—than the Garrison girls.

By the way, they—the Garrisons—suggested that we should sit at a small table with them, where they've already given a place to Jimmy. We accepted the invitation, and now we've just dined together. My frock was a dream; it's always nice

to come to the sort of hotel where one can wear
something pretty, as here and at Biarritz. Afterwards we all put on coats and cloaks and strolled
in the moonlight on the terrace. Jimmy tried to call
up from the "vasty deep" of his broken (?) heart the
spirit of the Past, with a capital P, but I would force
him into the track of automobilism instead. I don't
believe he knows a bit more than I do about it, if as
much, now that I've learned such a lot from the
Lightning Conductor, and if he takes to boasting
I'll just *show* him.

Now, good-night, my dear old Dad. I shall treat
myself to a "night-cap" draught of mountain air
before I go to bed on my balcony facing the Pyrenees.

Your

MOLLY-WHO-LOVES-ONLY-YOU.

FROM JACK WINSTON TO LORD LANE

Dear Safety Valve,

After the recent budget from Biarritz I had
no intention of inflicting another upon you—at least,
until we should reach Nice. But—there's as much
virtue in "but" as in "if"—you will be thinking in
Davos that it never rains but it pours letters; I am
thinking in Pau that it never rains but it pours young
men—Miss Randolph's young men. We've got
another one now, in his way as objectionable as
the first; and though I don't regard this specimen
as an active menace to the car, nor do I believe
he will resort to ripping up the tyres, he has his knife
into me.

Well, we arrived in Pau, which I know of old, and
in which I've had some rather jolly times, as Miss
Randolph would put it. Pau is the sort of place
where you meet your friends, and I scented danger,
but we were booked for only two days, and luck
had befriended me so well thus far that I trusted
it once more. I came to a hotel at some distance
from the Goddess's. Between two evils I chose the
less, and put my name down as "J. Winston," hoping
that if anyone knew me they wouldn't know Miss

Randolph, or *vice versâ*. Besides, I took counsel
with prudence, engaged a private sitting-room, and
ordered my meals sent up, to avoid being on show
in the *salle à manger*. All seemed serene, when
suddenly an adverse wind began to blow (as usual)
from an unexpected quarter.

Lured by fancied security, I took advantage of
that idleness for which Satan is popularly supposed
to provide mischief to put in a little private fun on
my own account. On the morning after our arrival
in Pau, Miss Randolph informed me that the car
and I would not be wanted, as she had met some
American friends and would be at their disposal
during the day. In an evil moment a golf rage
overpowered me, and I yielded, seeing no special
reason why I shouldn't. The Pau links are the best
on the Continent, and I had retained my membership
of the club from last year, when I was here with my
mother, so that was all right. I nicked into a cab
and told the man to drive to the golf club.

The steward remembered me, so did the professional; but as it was fairly early in the morning as
well as early in the season there were only a couple of
men in the smoking-room. I sat down to write a
letter at a corner table, and as one of the fellows was
talking in loud tones, advertising all the wares in
his shop windows, so to speak, I couldn't help
over-hearing what he said. He had one of those
objectionable, Anglo-maniac, American voices that
get on your nerves ; you know the snobbish sort
that, instead of being proud as punch of their own
country, want to appear more English than the

English, and get up for the part like an actor with all an actor's exaggerations. Well, this was one of those voices; and for all the owner might have taken his accent from his groom, he was mightily pleased with it.

I hadn't looked at the chap at first, but when I heard him telling his meek little exclamatory friend stories about a lot of my own friends (invariably making his impression by mentioning their titles first, then dropping into Christian names), I did take a glance at him over my shoulder.

I found him a curious combination of Sherlock Holmes and Little Lord Fauntleroy. He might have "gone on" at a moment's notice as understudy either for Mr. William Gillette in the one part, or for that clever little What's-his-name who resurrected the latter in London lately; though as for his dramatic talent, I've yet to judge, and may be called upon to do so, as you shall hear.

He went on gassing about all sorts of impossible feats he'd accomplished on a Panhard car, which he alluded to as his. According to himself, Fournier wasn't in it with him. Having heard to the end the tale of a motor race in which Sherlock-Fauntleroy, in company with the Duke of Bedford, had beaten King Edward the Seventh, the other man, deeply impressed, inquired through his nose (which he, being frankly Far-Western, didn't mind using as a channel of communication) whether his magnificent acquaintance was at present travelling on the famous Panhard, and had it with him.

"No," was the answer; "fact is I got a bit tired of

keeping the road, and lent my car to my old friend
Montie—Lord Lane, don't you know, who's running
it about the Riviera now."

Aha, my boy, does that make you sit up? I assure
you it did me. And if, just before, I hadn't heard
the gentleman discoursing on the pleasures of a
certain trip taken with Burford at a date when you
and Burford and I happened to be together, I should
have sat still straighter. I might have said to myself,
"So all is discovered. My Montie—or rather his
Montie—has taken a leaf out of Brown's book, and
instead of stuffing himself with fresh air and eggs at
Davos, is flashing about the Riviera in his dear
chum's Panhard, which he must have lately learnt
to drive, as he didn't know gearing from belts when
I saw him last." As it is, however, I assure you no
such suspicions are at present keeping me awake;
I've enough worries of my own to do that.

But Fauntleroy-Holmes was continuing, and I sat
in my obscure corner inhaling his tobacco smoke and
his equally ephemeral anecdotes

"I am going on to Nice myself in a day or two,
with some ladies, on their motor-car," said he. "Very
good car, I believe; one of the ladies very handsome.
She has a *chauffeur*, of course, but I shall drive and
let him do the dirty work. I fancy I shall be able to
show my friend something in the way of driving.
She wants to learn, and ought to have good instruc-
tion to begin with; one never recovers form if taught
bad ways at first."

I lay low, like Brer Rabbit, but my ears were
burning. He'd named no names, and I had no

reason to fit a cap on anybody's head. There were plenty of ladies and plenty of motor-cars in Pau, any of which might be going to Nice. I had never seen the man before, and didn't believe Miss Randolph knew him from Adam; still, I had a sensation of heat in my ears, and when I'd finished the letter I had begun (it was to Burford, by the way, but I refrained from telling him how his name had been taken in vain, less out of good nature than because I couldn't be bothered), I got up, went out, and asked the steward who the young man was who looked like Sherlock Holmes.

He knew at once who I meant, grinned, and informed me that the gentleman was a very rich American, named Payne, a great amateur auto-mobilist, and a keen golfer. How he had obtained all these particulars it wasn't difficult to guess, when one reflected upon Mr. Payne's fondness for talking of himself. By the way, have you ever met the man at all?

A few minutes after questioning the steward, I was strolling on the lawn thinking over what I had heard, when Sherlock walked out of the club, his obtrusive eyeglass dangling from his buttonhole.

He advanced towards me, somewhat to my surprise, and hailed me from afar, seeing, I suppose, that I was inclined to move on. "I say, sir," he began, "if you want a game, will you take me on? I've a friend just gone, and there doesn't seem to be anyone here but you and me——"

By this time he had stuck the big monocle in his eye, where it had somewhat the effect of a biscuit.

I fancied it was the addition of the eyeglass which discomposed his expression, but almost immediately I realised that the change was due to a cause more violent.

"B—ah Jove!" he ejaculated. And then, "'Pon my word, what damned impertinence!" He stood glaring at me through that eyeglass with such an "I am the Duke of Omnium, who the devil are you?" sort of expression that I thought he must be mad, and I stared also, in amazed silence.

After looking me up and down he began again. "What do you mean by it, I want to know, swaggering about here, among gentlemen, as if you were one of Us? I'll have you put out by the waiters." With this extraordinary outburst he turned on his heel, and was making off towards the club-house; but as you know, my temper is not of the sweetest, and mad or not mad, I didn't exactly yearn over Mr. Payne. I took advantage of the long legs about which "my friend Montie" has occasionally chaffed me and caught him up. I cannot conceal from you that I did more. I gripped him by the shoulder. I held him firmly, apparently somewhat against his will. I also shook him, and it now comes dimly back to me that his eyeglass jumped out of his eye.

"You damned cad!" I then remarked in a tone which some people might consider abrupt; "what in h—— do you mean?"

He took to stuttering—some men do in emergencies—and I knew from that instant that he couldn't drive a motor-car. "L—et go," he stammered like a schoolboy. "You—you—confounded *chauffeur*, you!

I'll tell your mistress of you, and have you discharged. You—you're Miss Randolph's *chauffeur*, and you come here to pass yourself off as a member at a gentleman's club."

On the point of knocking him down, I decided I wouldn't, and dropped him instead like a hot chestnut. You see, he "had me on the hip"; for I am Miss Randolph's *chauffeur*, and there was no good denying it. In a small way it was one of the nastiest situations of my life. What "A." in *Vanity Fair* would have done I don't know, and I didn't know what to do myself for a minute. You see, my prophetic soul tells me that the time hasn't come to confess all and throw myself on the Goddess's mercy, as I hope it may some day; and I couldn't afford to be plunged into hot water with her when the facts would look fishy and be impossible to explain. Still, I couldn't eat humble pie with that Bounder; sooner I would have quietly killed him, and stuffed him into a hole in the links. However, a sweet little cherub of inspiration looked out for the fate of poor Jack, and whispered an alternative in my ear.

"Do you dare deny it?" Payne demanded, plucking up courage.

"I 'dare' do a good deal," said I, looking him straight in the eyes. "But I don't intend to deny it. I am Miss Randolph's *chauffeur*." How he had found that out I couldn't imagine.

"Then, I can tell you, you won't long remain so," blustered the fellow, as cocksure as if he were her brother, or something nearer—hang him! "A man who is capable of practising such deception isn't fit to be trusted with a lady. I shall get you the sack."

"You ought to be a good judge of deception," said I. "Have you told Miss Randolph yet about that trip of yours with the Duke of Burford last summer?"

Sherlock-Fauntleroy got as red as a beet, and the Fauntleroy characteristics predominated. I thought tears were about to start from his eyes, but he merely relapsed into another fit of the stutters. "Wh—hat d—do you mean?" he chattered. "Y—you don't know what you're talking about."

"Oh yes, I do," I said, growing calmer as he grew excited, "a good deal more than you knew what you were talking about when you claimed the Duke as your friend. I happened to be with him at the time last summer, when you said you were driving him on your car."

"*You* with the Duke!" sneered Sherlock. "Who would believe that?"

"Miss Randolph would," said I. "The Duke of Burford was driving his own car last summer. Now you can guess how I happened to be with him. There was just one other man on board; your friend Montie, Lord Lane, you know. Lord Lane was another of my old masters." (Hope you don't object to being referred to as an Old Master, and I *was* your fag at Eton.) "I know him very well. He can do a good many things, can Lord Lane, but he can't drive a motor-car. And another little detail you've got wrong. He isn't running about on the Riviera. He is at Davos Platz. I've had a letter from him there the other day; he's very thoughtful of his old servants. Miss Randolph would think it queer if you said you expected to meet Lord Lane on the Riviera with your car, and I showed her a letter from him which proved he'd been at Davos for the last six weeks. Or he wouldn't mind telegraphing if I wired."

"You're a regular blackmailer," gasped Payne.

"Not at all," said I. "I suggest a bargain, but I don't want money. All I want is not to lose my job. Don't you give me away, and I won't give you away. Do you agree to that compromise and no more said?"

We had been holding each other by the eye, but suddenly his wandered, assisted by the monocle. So odd an expression sat on his face that I followed his straying glance, and saw what he saw—Miss Randolph! Miss Randolph at one of the long French windows of the club-house, with several other ladies. Without a second's hesitation I gripped Payne by the arm and dragged him across the lawn, using him as a screen. Once round the corner of the house, I let him go; but I dared not wait to chaffer. "Remember, it's a bargain," I reminded the fellow. "While you keep to your part I keep to mine, and not a moment longer." With this I darted into one of the waiting cabs. That was a narrow shave, but I congratulated myself that I had come out of it "on top," joyful in the hope that I should snatch Miss Randolph away in a day or two, and the episode would be closed. But mice and men should go slow in self-congratulation. Even a confirmed liar occa-

sionally tells the truth by mistake. Next day
(which means to-day) I learned this through bitter
experience. Nothing had happened, and when I
presented myself to Miss Randolph in the morning
for orders, her manner was so pleasant, so exactly
the same as usual, that I made sure Mr. Payne
had chosen the better part of valour and held his
peace. Evening came, however; my mistress sent
for me, as I was informed through the invaluable
hall-porter. Coward conscience, or some other intricate internal organ, gave a twinge. I asked myself
blankly if I had been betrayed, if I were in for a
scolding, if I should have to choose between being
ignominiously chucked out of my precious berth, or
prematurely owning up to the trick I have played,
with the consequent risk of losing my lady forever.
I felt pretty sick as I went up the servants' stairs to
Miss Randolph's floor at the "Gassisn" and knocked
at the door of her private sitting-room.

The door was on the latch, and as I tapped I heard
Aunt Mary exclaim in a tone of extreme scorn, "Ask
him '*if he objects*,' indeed! One would think *you*
were the servant and he the master. You shall do
nothing of the kind."

My knocking evidently cut short the argument.
Miss Randolph called "Come in!" and I obeyed, all
black leather and humility. I hardly raised my eyes
to the ladies, yet I saw that She was looking adorable
in a white dress, with nothing but sparkling lacey
stuff over the loveliest neck and arms on earth. She
smiled, so I hoped that my sin had not found me out,
but it was not precisely one of her own frank, starry

smiles; there was something new and constrained, and my heart still misgave me.

"Brown," said she (and I observed that Aunt Mary had fixed her with a threatening eye), "Brown, I thought I'd send for you to say that we'll have another passenger to-morrow for a few days. Or that is we may have to ask him to drive sometimes, out of politeness, for I believe he's a good driver, and he might be hurt if we didn't; though I'm *sure* he drives no better than you."

By this time I knew what was coming, and steeled myself to bear it, but there might have been a certain involunatry elongation of countenance, for the poor child rushed into explanations to save my battered feelings. "You see," she went on, "this gentleman, Mr. Payne, is a very old friend of the family, and he has been travelling in Europe a long time, for a rest. He overworked himself or something, and broke down. Now, he has lent his car to an English friend of his, Lord Lane, whom he arranged to rejoin on the Riviera. But he doesn't feel well, and railway travelling disagrees with him. His doctor here has just told him that he must be continually in the open air if he doesn't want to have a relapse; and Miss Kedison thinks my father would be annoyed if we didn't ask him to drive with us, as we are going the way he must go. The Napier is such a fine car, I suppose it can take four as well as three, and a little more luggage?"

"Oh yes, miss, there'll be no difficulty about that," I answered grudgingly.

"And you won't feel that it is lack of trust in you, if he drives part of the time?"

At this Aunt Mary glared, but that Angel paid not the slightest attention.

There is an unwritten law that a man shall not be a brute; and after her sweet consideration of my chauffery feelings I couldn't show myself ungracious. I assured her that I should not feel hurt, and that she was very kind to think of me at all. I would do my best for the party, unless, of course, my services would be superfluous, now that she was to be accompanied by a friend who was a competent driver.

I wonder what I *should* have done in the unlikely event that she took me at my word? Picture my feelings, bereft of my Goddess, bereft of my Napier at one and the same time, constrained to resignation, while a confounded impostor drove off with both from under my very nose! Miss Randolph hastened to deny any such thought, and to impress upon me my value as a *chauffeur*. But things are bad enough as they are.

Here I am saddled with a fellow who hates me as a cur hates a man who has thrashed him, and will snap if he dares. Instead of turning my back upon him, I have to carry him away on it; and if a rod isn't in pickle for me, I'm not

Your old friend,

JACK WINSTON.

FROM JACK WINSTON TO LORD LANE

Dear Montie,

I can't let you alone, you see. I must unburden myself, or something will happen—something
apoplectic. If I have sinned, I am punished; and
so far as I can see the worst still stretches before me
in a long vista. It was good of you to scrawl off
that second letter, at midnight, as an afterthought.
It was forwarded, and has just reached me here, by
grand good luck.

You say I would do better to make a clean breast
of it; but that's easier said than done. You're not
here, and you can't see the "lie of the land" as I can.
I'll explain the position to you, from my point of
view, for I think you don't quite understand it.

Not to mince matters, I am a Fraud, and Miss
Randolph is the sort of girl to resent being imposed
upon, If this Payne, who rejoices in the name of
Jimmy, should find out the truth about me and tell
her to-morrow, she would be exceedingly angry, as
she would have a right to be, and would, I think,
find it hard to forgive me. It is because I have felt
this instinctively that I have let things slide. I have
drifted down the stream of enjoyment, saying to the
passing hour, like Goethe's hero, "Stay, thou art

172

fair," though too often the thought would present itself that this could not go on for ever. Besides, there were drawbacks, big or little, according to my mood. I have always kept it before myself, more or less, that some day Miss Randolph would dispense with me and my car, in the natural course of affairs, even if the event were not hastened by some *contretemps* or other; and that it might then be as difficult to adjust matters as it is now. But in truth I hope it won't be so. What I aim to do is to make myself so indispensable to her as Brown that she can't bring herself to get on without me as Jack Winston. I haven't done that yet, though it isn't for lack of trying; therefore I'm not ready for the crisis, and therefore I'm afraid of Payne. Yes, "afraid," that's the word. And my one consolation is that he's equally afraid of me.

Your ordinary, habitual liar can bear up if he's found out, and laugh it off somehow, but your snob and boaster can't. This man could hardly survive being stripped of his dukes and earls, with which he's covered his untitled nakedness as with a mantle, for the eyes of Miss Randolph. In this natural phenomenon lies my chance of gaining time, and other things that I want.

You would have had some pure enjoyment out of to-day if you had been the fifth person on my Napier. If you could have heard Aunt Mary (who, in common with a certain type of American, worships a title and rolls it on her tongue as if it were a plover's egg out of season) asking "Jimmy" questions about his grand English friends! Knowing that my cold and venomous eye was upon him, and writhing under it, he had to answer her questions. "What sort of looking man is the Duke of Burford, Jimmy? Did you ever stay at any of his country places? Is it true that he often entertains the Royalties? Were you ever asked to a house-party to meet the King and Queen?"

I could almost have found it in my heart to pity him; but my interests at stake were too big for me to have derived the serene pleasure from the situation that you might have enjoyed as an initiated outsider. But with my attempted explanations and my chortlings I've digressed too much, and I'll get back to "Hecuba."

We started from the "Gassion." Miss Randolph announced that she would drive at first. This was, I judged, a sop for me, as Cerberus. But Payne was given the seat of honour beside her, and I was relegated to the *tonneau* with Aunt Mary and the other impedimenta. My day was over!

Miss Kedison considers it *infra dig.* to converse with a servant, though she has been content often enough to use me as a guide-book. She doesn't like sitting in front, so she was obliged to put up with my physical nearness, but she took pains to emphasise her soul's remoteness. I think her opinion of me has been for some time that I am "too big for my boots," and I was not surprised to learn that it was by her advice Mr. Payne had been invited to join the party. No doubt she thought it would put me in my proper place, and so it has. Besides, we had not been long *en route* when I gleaned from several indications, small in themselves, that "Jimmy" is a great favourite with her, so great that she would not object to becoming his aunt by marriage. They are warm friends, and if he hasn't already poured into her ear confidences prejudicial to me, there, I fear, lies danger for the future.

We had not been gone long from Pau before Miss Randolph glanced round at me—a risky thing to do when you're driving; but the road was straight and clear as far as the eye could see. I was half in hopes she would request me to drive; but not so. "By the way, Brown," said she, "I forgot to ask; didn't I see you at the golf club the other day?"

From the form of the question I couldn't tell whether Payne had played the sneak or not, nor could I guess from her face, as she had turned to business again. As for him, he had ignored me haughtily since the start.

"*Me*, miss, at the golf club?" I promptly protested, regardless of grammar and not sure I wasn't in for an explosion which would blow poor Brown sky-high; "why, a *chauffeur* wouldn't be admitted there."

"I suppose not," she answered over her shoulder. "But there was a man very like you when my friends took me—and walking with Mr. Payne, too."

"Now for it!" thought I. But then Jimmy's first words reassured me. "Oh, I don't know all the strangers one talks to at a club," he replied in haste; and then, by way of changing the subject, the bounder asked Miss Randolph if she wouldn't let him drive. "It's over a hundred miles to Toulouse.

and you'll want a firm hand, for the days are short,"
he had the impudence to add.

At that I lost my head, and made a big mistake.
I felt I couldn't stand sitting still while he tried
experiments with my car, and almost before I knew
what I was doing I blurted out, "Beg pardon, miss,
but are you sure this gentleman understands driving
a Napier? My master expected that *I* was to drive
his car when he let it out, and——"

Such a look of reproach as the Goddess threw me!
"But *I* understand that, while I hire the car it is
mine to do as I like with, in reason," she cut me
short. "Mr. Payne tells me that he has often driven
his friend the Duke of Burford's Napier. And if
anything happens to your master's car while I have
it, I will pay for the damage up to its full value, so
your mind may be at ease on his account."

With this well-deserved, but none the less crushing
snub she brought the car to a standstill and inadvertently stopped the motor. After virtually agreeing the night before to let Payne drive, I ought
to have kept my mouth shut; but you will admit
that the temptation was strong. I descended, like
a well-conducted *chauffeur*, to help my mistress
change places with my hated rival, and of course
it was my duty to start the motor again, which I did.
Before I could get out of the way, Payne started—
on the third speed, like the duffer he is, changing
so quickly to the second that I had to race after the
car and hurl myself into the *tonneau* to avoid being
left behind. In doing this I unfortunately trod on
Aunt Mary's toes. She groaned, glared, and mut-

tered only half below her breath, "Clumsy creature!"
Thoroughly humiliated, and no longer in a mood to
care whether their Jimmy wrecked the car and
killed us (all but one) I took my seat. I do believe
that Aunt Mary secretly thinks me capable of having
misjudged and ill-treated Eyelashes, who laid himself out to "be nice" to her.

Hardly had we started when I heard Miss Randolph telling Payne that this car belonged to the
Honourable John Winston, Lord Brighthelmston's
son, and asking him if he had ever met Mr. Winston.
I suppose that, in the excitement of managing a
big machine which he knew little or nothing about,
Payne forgot that, since I "went with the car," the
owner must have been one of those (to him) fatal
old masters of mine. He can't bear to deny the
soft impeachment of knowing anyone whom he
thinks may be a swell, and in the hurry of the moment habit got the better of prudence.

"Oh yes, I know Jack very well!" he exclaimed;
then drew in his breath with a little gasp which he
turned into a cough. In that moment he had
probably remembered me.

"I suppose you know his mother, then?" said Miss
Randolph. "I met her in Paris. She's at Cannes
now, and so you will see her there."

"Ye—es," returned Jimmy. "Oh yes, I shall
certainly see her. I know Lord Brighthelmston
better than I do her; but I shall call, of course."

What with his fear of having committed himself
anew, and the chill in his marrow produced by my
critical eye on his vertebræ, he grew more and more

nervous, wobbling whenever there was a delicate
piece of steering to be done or a restive horse to
be passed. He changed speeds so clumsily that the
pinions went together with a crash each time, and
shivers ran up and down my spine when I heard the
noise and thought of the damage this conceited idiot
might do to my poor gears. Could *you* stand by
like Patience on the lee cathead, smiling at a wet
swab, while some duffer with a whip and spurs
bestrode your favourite stallion, Roland? Perhaps
that simile will help you to understand how I've been
feeling all day.

Payne is a rank amateur. I doubt if he ever
drove a Napier before, and would bet something he
depended for his success to-day (such as it was) on
keen observation of everything Miss Randolph did
before he took the helm. He knows how to steer
a moderately straight course and to change speeds—
that's about all; and I wouldn't trust his nerve in
an emergency. However, we bowled along without
incident through Tarbes and Tournay, thanks more
to the fine car than the driver; but when mounting
a long stretch of steep road beyond a place called
Lanespède, where a great railway viaduct crosses the
valley, Payne missed his change, and then completely
lost his head, failing to put on the brakes to prevent
us running down the hill backwards. Luckily I was
sitting on the brake side, and reaching out of the
tonneau, I seized the lever of the hand-brake and
jammed it on. Next instant (to make quite sure)
I jumped out, ran to the front, and lowered the
sprag. I don't think any of them knew what a

narrow escape we'd had, and Payne covered himself
by abusing the car. We started up again on the
second, and came out on an undulating plain overlooking a little watering-place called Capvern-les-
Bains, lying far below in a dimple of the Pyrenean
foothills.

There was no other incident till we came to Mon-
tréjeau, where my road-book showed that there
was an uncommonly steep hill. So I ventured to
say over Payne's shoulder, "Better look out here,
sir; a bad hill." The cad had not the civility to
notice my warning, but charged through the long
street of the town till he came to the verge of a
dangerous descent, dipping steeply and suddenly for
a little way, then turning abruptly to the left. He
was taking the hill at a reckless pace, not because
he was plucky, but because he knew no better; and
half-way down, seeing a lumbering station-omnibus
climbing slowly up, not leaving much room, he began
to get wild in his steering. Again I hung out, and
gently but firmly put on the hand-brake, steadying
the car. The idiot didn't even see how I had saved
him, for when we got safely down he said to Miss
Randolph, "Took that hill flying, didn't I?" I can
tell you I was glad when we pulled up for luncheon
at St. Gaudens, knowing that the road here turns
away from the Pyrenees to cross the great plain of
Languedoc.

Blessed plain of Languedoc, which has been abused
by some travellers for its monotony! Sitting silently
in the *tonneau* with Aunt Mary, I revelled in the
long, straight level of wide, poplar-fringed road that

stretched as far as the eye could reach, running up
to a point in the distant perspective. "Here, at any
rate," I reflected, "the duffer at the wheel can't do us
much harm." It was a beautiful scene, had I been
in tune to enjoy it, for the Pyrenees showed their
blue outlines on the far horizon, and the Garonne
gave us many pictures near at hand. There was in
particular one sweet sylvan "bit" at a place called
St. Martory, which, though it was but a fleeting
glimpse, framed itself in my mind with all the pre-
cision of a stereoscopic view.

It was a relief to me, when this evening, we ran
into Toulouse; its many buildings of brick lying
along the bank of the broad and peaceful Garonne,
looking curiously rose-hued in the level rays of the
declining sun.

But poor car! when I set to work at cleaning it
after its ill-treatment it seemed to reproach me for
disloyalty. Its very lamps were like mournful, misunderstood eyes. And this is only the first day of
many. How long, O friend, how long? I don't
quite see what is to become of your unfortunate

JACK WINSTON.

NARBONNE, *December* 17.

I didn't post the beginning of this letter. I felt
I should want to add something.

Another day has passed—a day of alarms and
excursions. Payne has made an ass of himself,
and I have scored off him, winning my way back
to the front seat of the car, and relegating him to

the *tonneau* with Aunt Mary. But I have not shaken
him off. He's still in our pocket, and to all appearance means to stick there. The situation, therefore,
remains essentially what it was yesterday.

But for the incident of which I will tell you, this
might have been one of the most delightful bits of the
whole tour. Even though at first I was stuffed into
the *tonneau*, I couldn't help finding pleasure in the
pictures through which we flashed in the earlier part
of the day.

There was a good deal of *pavé* to traverse before we
were clear of Toulouse, and then we came into a fine,
open world, chasing and passing many peasants'
carts. These always occupy the middle of the road,
and as their drivers are often asleep, there is much
blowing of the horn and shouting before they pull
over to their right side. Presently we found out the
meaning of this stream of carts, for we ran into a
large village with turkeys and geese all over the road,
like carpet bedding, tied by the legs and cackling
loudly. There were crowds of peasants—old and
young; the old women with neat, black silk head-
dresses framing their brown, wrinkled faces; and
through the midst of this animated scene we had to
drive at a foot-pace, tootling on the horn. On the
other side of the long village we found ourselves on
a wide, level road, that for smoothness would shame a
billiard-table, crossed the green Canal du Midi, and
ran for a while by its side, passing a queer obelisk
erected to Riquet, its constructor.

Suddenly, on mounting a hill, an enormous view
spread out before us. The distant Pyrenees showed

their serrated line far away to the right, their snowy
tops spectral over an intervening range of hills; to
the left stretched a vast, undulating tract of country,
with towns and church spires distinctly outlined in
the clear, crisp air—for it was a day of glorious
lights.   Beyond all was a range of vague, blue hills
which I knew to be the Cevennes, sacred to the
memory of Robert Louis Stevenson.

We sped through village after village—a long
street; children in blouses playing strange games,
disputing in shrill voices, wagging little eloquent
fingers under each other's noses; handsome men
clothed in blue, with red sashes and the universal
berret on their heads, guiding with their cruel goads
patient teams of yoked oxen; a group of persons
round a church door—a wedding, perhaps a funeral;
old women knitting in the sun, young women smiling
from windows—all these impressions follow each
other like flickering pictures in a cinematograph;
and then with the last flicker one is out again on the
broad, white road, with the flying trees spinning by
on either hand, and the white, filmy clouds floating
in an azure sky.   It is only on the motor-car that you
get all these sensations.   In a train you are in a box;
on a motor you are in a chariot of fire with the wide
heavens open above you.

At Castelnaudary there was another scene of ani-
mation, for here also it was market day; and though
it was only twenty miles or so on to Carcassonne (our
intended destination), my betters decided that they
would take luncheon at the hotel in Castelnaudary.
For the first time since Payne has been with us Miss

Randolph seemed to wish to restore me to my old, lost footing. "You must lunch with us, Brown," she said, with a smile that goes straight to one's heart. But I was not in a gracious mood. I had had enough of Aunt Mary; I could not stand the haughty Payne. I answered, therefore, rather shortly. There were certain adjustments to be done on the car which would occupy some time, I said, and I would take my luncheon later. Her poor little friendly smile went out, like a lamp extinguished. For an instant she lingered, then turned away without a word, and I could have bitten out my own surly tongue.

To justify myself I pottered with the car, then went moping off to another hotel, and tried to restore my lost spirits with *paté de foie de canard* and fresh walnuts, which would have delighted the palate of a happier man.

At it was I had neither the heart nor the stomach to linger over the feast, and consequently got back long before the others were ready for me. *They* didn't hurry themselves. I promise you. While busying myself in flicking dust off the car, a courteous little crowd assembled and questioned me as to the make of the car (expressing surprise when they heard it was all English, even to the tyres) and as to how far I had come. When I said "From Dieppe *via* Biarritz" a murmur of respect rippled to the outer edge of the group, and at this moment my party appeared.

Payne wore a swaggering air, and looked now like Little Lord Fauntleroy gone wrong. He was far too

big a man to notice me, or any of the kindly, simple
people who had been admiring the car, and came up
with us, talking his loudest to Aunt Mary. He almost
elbowed me aside, and got into the driver's seat as a
matter of course. Perhaps he had looked upon the
rich wine of the country when it was red, though
I didn't think of that at the time, and attributed
his exaggerated insolence to natural cussedness of
soul.

We swept away from the hotel with a curve, which
isn't a line of beauty for a motor-car, and as we left
the town Jimmy's conception of his part as driver
became so eccentric that Miss Randolph looked
worried—that is, her pretty shoulders stiffened themselves; I couldn't often see her face—and Aunt Mary
more than once gave vent to a frightened squeak.
Once, in her extremity as we shaved the wheel of
a passing cart, she unbent so far as to throw an
appealing glance at me. But I sat in stony silence
with crossed arms, looking oblivious to all that went
on and somewhat resembling, I flattered myself,
portraits of Napoleon beholding the burning of
Moscow.

On the high road Jimmy began to recover his form
—if it be worth the name—but, as if to show that he
was all right, and never had been otherwise, he put
the car at its quickest pace, which was so far from
safe on a road dotted with carts that I began to
expect trouble; and if it hadn't been for Miss Randolph, to see my expectation fulfilled would have
pleased the baser part of me Once or twice a cart-
load of peasants scowled savagely at us as we rushed

past on our headlong career, and at length I had the satisfaction of hearing Miss Randolph rather stiffly suggest that Jimmy should moderate the pace. He obeyed with a laugh, which he meant to be recklessly brave, yet indulgent to the weaknesses of women; but in my ears it only sounded silly. At this moment a two-wheeled cart with five peasants in it—three men and two women—came in sight.

As soon as they saw us one of the men—a big, black-browed fellow—held up his hand imperatively in warning. Another fine, muscular chap jumped down and ran to the horse's head. Anyone with a grain of sense or consideration, on seeing these signals, would have slowed down, and if necessary have stopped the engine altogether; but though I heard Miss Randolph beg him to go slow, Sherlock-Fauntleroy held right on at a good twenty-five miles an hour.

In a moment or two we had come level with the cart, and the horse bolted. The man leading it was thrown violently to the ground, and the cart went over him. Luckily he tucked in his head and drew up his feet, or he would have been shockingly hurt, perhaps killed. He lay a moment or two, half stunned with the shock, while the horse galloped away, dragging after him the swaying cart, the two women screaming at the top of their voices. The man driving managed to pull up the frightened animals some way down the road, and the people in the cart scrambled out to help their fallen friend, who meanwhile had picked himself up, and pale with fright and passion, blood streaming down his face, was limping after the car gesticulating violently.

Payne had not turned his head, and the moment that a startled "Oh!" from Miss Randolph told him there had been an accident he put on speed, clearly with the intention of avoiding a row. The injured man stooped to pick up a stone. At the same instant Miss Randolph, in her most imperious manner (and she can be imperious), commanded Payne to stop instantly and go back. "But we shall have the whole pack of them on us like wolves," he objected. *"Go back!"* she repeated, stamping her little foot. "I won't hurt a man and drive away." Suddenly Payne pulled up, and putting in the reverse, we ran slowly into the midst of the horde of angry peasants, swollen now by many others who had been passing along the crowded road.

As we backed into that sea of scowling faces I thought of the various revolutions France has seen. It was like stirring up a wasps' nest. Everyone was yelling at once. In the front rank stood the man who had been knocked down, his trousers cut to tatters. He had lashed himself into such a fury that he had become almost incoherent, and the flood of speech which rushed from his white lips was more like the yells of an animal than the ordered utterance of a human being. By his side were the two women who had been in the cart, both sobbing and screaming, while everyone else in the angry mob shouted simultaneously. Aunt Mary went very pale; Payne looked upon his handiwork with a sulky grin; but Miss Randolph took the business in hand with the greatest pluck. She had whisked off her veil and faced the people boldly, her grey eyes meeting theirs, her face white, save for a bright pink spot on either cheek. At sight of her beauty the clamour died down, and in the lull she spoke to the man who had been thrown under the horse.

"I am very sorry you are hurt," she said, "and shall be pleased to give you something to buy yourself new clothes. Are you injured anywhere?"

At the sound of her correct but foreign-sounding French someone in the crowd shouted out, "*A bas les Anglais!*" The girl drew herself up proudly and looked in the direction of the voice. She didn't try to excuse herself by denying England and claiming a nationality more popular in France, and I loved her more than ever for this reticence.

"Pay!" shouted the man who had been hurt, with one hand wiping a trickle of blood out of his eye, with the other thumping the mud-guard of the car. "Of course you shall pay. God only knows what injuries I have received. *Mazette!* I am all one ache. Ah, you pay well, or you do not go on!" He pressed closer to the car, and his friends closed in around him.

"Pay them, Molly! pay anything they ask!" quavered Aunt Mary, "or they will kill us! Oh, I always knew something like this was bound to happen! What a fool I was to leave my peaceful home and come to a country of thieves and murderers!"

"Don't be frightened, Aunt Mary," said the girl, with more patience for her relative's garrulous complaints than I had. Then she turned to me. "Brown, is that man much hurt?" she asked briskly.

"No," I replied. "He is merely scratched, and no doubt bruised. If he had any bones broken, any internal injury or] severe strain, he couldn't rage about like a mad bull."

"Still, it was our fault," she said. "We ought to have stopped. His clothes are torn. How much ought we to pay?"

"Nothing at all," said Sherlock. "Don't you let yourself be blackmailed."

She didn't answer or look in his direction, thus emphasising the fact that she had asked her question of me, not of him.

"Fifty francs would be generous," I said, "to buy the fellow a new suit of clothes and pay for a bottle of liniment. With that to-morrow he would be thanking his stars for the accident. But as Mr. Payne was driving, hadn't you better let him talk to them? It isn't right that two men should stand by and let the burden fall on a lady."

"*You* speak to them, Brown; I give you *carte blanche*," said she, and we faced the mob together.

"If you threaten us," I said, "you shall have nothing. We were going fast, but your horse is badly broken, and is more of a danger on the road than an automobile. If you behave yourself and tell your friends to do likewise, this lady wishes to give you fifty francs to buy new clothes in place of those which have suffered in this accident. But we don't intend to be bullied."

"Fifty francs!" shrieked the man. "Fifty francs

for a man's life! Bah! You aristocrats! Five hundred francs; not a sou less, or you do not stir from this place. Fifty francs! *Mazette!*"

"You are talking nonsense, and you know it," said I roughly. "Stand out of our way, or we will send for the police."

Now this was bluff, for the last thing to be desired was the presence of the police. I had been careful to get in Paris the necessary *permis de conduire* from the Department of Mines, without which it is illegal to drive a motor vehicle of any sort in France. But I had heard Payne boasting to Miss Randolph that he never bothered himself about a lot of useless red tape; it was only milksops and amateurs who did that. I, as Brown, had kept "my master's" papers, but it would do more harm than good to our cause, should it come to an investigation, if I attempted to pass over my permit to Payne. Were the police to appear on the scene their first demand would be for papers, and if the man who had been driving were unable to produce any, not all our just complaints of the peasants' unlawful threats would help us. Payne would be liable to arrest and imprisonment; not only would he be heavily fined, but we should all be detained, perhaps for weeks; and as French magistrates have as strong a prejudice against the automobile as their English brothers, especially when the offender is a foreigner, it might go hard with everyone concerned. This would be a dismal interruption of our tour, and if I hadn't felt sure that the enemy would be in as great a funk of the police as we were, I wouldn't have ventured on so bold a bluff. I trembled internally for an instant as to its success, but as usual in life and poker, it paid.

"No, you don't!" shouted not the one peasant, but many in chorus, as unlike the merry peasant-chorus of light opera as you can imagine. "We won't have the police. We attend to this affair ourselves."

And it began to look as if they meant to. "Give the five hundred francs, or you will be sorry!" they yelled, and again, in a second, they were all surging round us, threatening with their fists, snatching out their pocket-knives, and I saw things were getting hot. A French crowd barks a good deal before it bites, but this one had come to the biting stage. We were far from town and the police, even if the latter wouldn't have done us more harm than good. Here we had Miss Randolph and Miss Kedison. If Payne were as useless as I judged him, I was one man against forty.

The two ladies were still on the car. Payne had got off at first, but had slipped back when things began to be lively. I alone was on the ground, close to the bonnet, so that if needful I could protect the motor and Miss Randolph at the same time.

The crowd consulted an instant, then stampeded the car. Aunt Mary shrieked, and threw out her purse, as if she flung a live lamb to hungry wolves. The motor was going still, but to charge into the crowd might mean killing a dozen wretched peasants. It was out of the question, but something must be done, and now was the moment for doing it. One fellow tried to snatch a sable rug off Miss Kedison's knees; I struck his hand away, and sent him staggering. Then I yelled to Payne to get into the *tonneau*. There was no more pride left in him than in a rag, and he crawled over, like a dog. Meanwhile, I'd made up my mind what to do, and was going to try an experiment as our best chance to get out of the town without bloodshed.

I knew that a union which held the exhaust pipe in place on the silencer had been working loose. I grabbed a spanner out of the tool-box, and elbowing my way along the side of the car again, with two turns of the spanner loosened the union, pushed forward the throttle-lever in the steering-post, and gave the motor all its gas.

The thing was done in a quarter the time it's taken me to write of it, and you can guess the effect. Bang! bang! came a succession of explosions quick and pitiless as a Maxim gun. Those peasants gave way like wheat before the scythe. I don't doubt they thought they were shot and on the way to kingdom come; and before they'd time to find out their mistake I was up on the step, had seized the steering-wheel, and started the car. We were on a slight decline, and the good steed bounded forward at the rate of fifteen miles an hour. An instant later I slipped in the fourth, and we were going forty-five.

When the enemy saw how they'd been tricked, which they did in about six seconds, they were after us with a howl. A shower of stones fell harmlessly on the road behind us, angry yells were drowned in the hideous noise of the exhaust. We could afford to laugh at the thought of pursuit. But there was another side to the story. Now that there was no

one on the spot to complain of their threats of
violence, they could safely apply to the police and
make a bold stroke for vengeance, just as we had for
escape. However, there was no use in thinking of
that for the moment; I had done the best I could
and must go on doing it. No normal tympanum
could stand the racket of the exhaust for long, and
Miss Randolph and Miss Kedison were sitting with
their hands over their ears, the lower part of Aunt
Mary's face under her mask expressing a comical
horror. I caught sight of her visage when I stopped
the car (which I did as soon as we were beyond
danger of pursuit) to fasten up the silencer again;
and it was all I could do not to laugh.

The fastening-up business was an affair of two or
three minutes, and at first the three sat in shocked
silence, their heads dazed by the late ear-splitting
din. Then, the cool peace of welcome silence was
broken by Mr. Payne. "I consider," he said stiffly
to Miss Randolph, "that your *mécanicien* has behaved with unwarrantable insolence in ordering
me——"

"And I consider that he saved the situation," cut
in the *mécanicien's* mistress.

"I acted for what I thought the best, miss; there
wasn't much time to decide," said I, with a sleek
humility which I assume on occasions. "If I have
given offence, I am sorry," I went on, looking at her
and not at Payne.

"You haven't given offence," she said. "I am
sure Mr. Payne, when he comes to reflect, will see
that you did yeoman's service. But what is to

happen now? I suppose we're not safe from trouble yet, and we don't deserve to be."

I thought it rather sporting of her to say "we," when all the bother was due to the conceit and cock-sureness of one person.

"No, miss, we don't deserve to be, if you'll excuse the liberty," I meekly replied. "We had no business charging along a crowded road the way we did. I'm sure, until to-day, we've never had anything but courtesy from people of all classes. It isn't often French peasants misbehave themselves, and to-day most of the wrong was on our side, though it's true that their horse was skittish; and being market-day, I daresay they'd taken a little more red wine than was good for them. The wine of this country is apt to go to the head."

I spoke to Miss Randolph, but *at* Jimmy, especially when I gave that dig about the wine. I finished my tirade and my work on the silencer at the same time, and it was then that my triumph came. Instead of getting back on the car, I stood still in the road.

"What are you waiting for?" asked Miss Randolph.

"For Mr. Payne to take his place in the driver's seat," said I.

At this he half jumped up in the *tonneau*, but Miss Randolph hurriedly exclaimed, "Oh, I think you had better drive for a while, Brown. I want to talk to you, and ask you what to do, and what will happen next." Little Lord Fauntleroy, with every Sher-lockian characteristic temporarily obliterated, sat down again in the *tonneau* pouting.

We had not wasted five minutes, and now we sprang forward at a good speed for Carcassonne.

"What will happen next," I said, answering Miss Randolph's question, "may be this. If the peasants are angry enough to take the trouble and risk, all they have to do is to go to the police-station in the nearest village and give information against us, when a wire with a description of us and the car will raise the whole country so that we shall not be safe anywhere."

"Oh, my gracious!" the poor child exclaimed. "What are we to do? Aunt Mary and I have other hats and jackets and things in our car-luggage. Couldn't we change, so as to look quite different, and buy a lot of—of Aspinall, or something in the next village before they've had time to give the alarm, and paint the poor car a bright scarlet? Then we should get through and no one would know."

I couldn't help laughing, though really her suggestion wasn't so fantastic as it may sound, for I know a man who did that very trick in somewhat similar circumstances; but her earnestness combined with the childlike guile on her face was comic.

"It would be too long a job to paint the car before we could be spotted," I said. "I think we must just hope for the best, and show a bold face. I shouldn't be surprised if we'd get through all right somehow. Perhaps, if there was much money in your aunt's purse, miss, the peasants would prefer keeping their mouths shut and sticking to that than mixing themselves up with the police and perhaps losing what they might have had, like the dog with his meat in the fable."

"There were about a hundred francs in my purse," announced Aunt Mary.

"If they do catch us, what then?" the girl asked.

I explained the state of the case as I had argued it out to myself.

"Oh, well," sighed Miss Randolph, "I suppose we can't do better than take your advice, but this isn't a nice adventure. I do hate feeling guilty—like an escaping criminal, with every hand against me. And I *loathe* suspense; I always want to know the worst. When shall we be sure what the peasants have made up their minds to do?"

"Well," I said, "in less than an hour, if all goes well, we ought to be at the *octroi* station outside Carcassonne, and if we are 'wanted' by the police we shall know it fast enough, because they will—er— try to stop us there."

"Then I hope all *won't* go well," moaned Miss Randolph. She who had been so brave when forty peasants threatened us with words, stones, and even knives, was crushed under the vague menace of the law. "If only we could arrive after dark we might flash through before the *octroi* people knew. *Let's* arrive after dark," she exclaimed eagerly. "It's getting on towards four now. Let's stop—since we've been perfectly certain for ages that no one was attempting to follow us—and—and deliberately have tea by the roadside. If we do that we can easily pass the time, so as not to arrive at the *octroi* until half-past five, when it will be dark. It's moonlight, but the moon doesn't rise now till six or after."

"We could do that certainly," I said, "and we

might get through without being nabbed. If we succeed, we might rush on through Carcassonne, instead of stopping there to-night; for the farther away we get and the more towns we can say we've passed through without being detained, the better for our chances of ultimate escape."

"But I don't want to miss Carcassonne," she objected. "You've told me so much about the place that I've been looking forward to it more than to almost anything else."

So had I, if the truth were known, but I had looked forward to visiting Carcassonne with her before I had "drunk and seen the spider." In other words, before Mr. Payne had joined our party. However, I couldn't bear to have her disappointed, for his fault, too; besides, I'm vain enough to like hearing from her lips the flattering words, "Brown, you are so resourceful!" Therefore I stirred up my brains in the effort to be resourceful now.

"We might hide the car in Carcassonne if we could once get in," I mysteriously suggested; "then you could steal up on foot to the *cité* by moonlight, and when you'd had your fill of sight-seeing steal back to the car again and make a rush for it."

"Splendid!" cried Miss Randolph, clapping her hands. Behold, I had made a hit!

The car was stopped, the tea-basket got out, and who so indispensable as the late despised Brown? Brown it was who went to a cottage hard by and procured drinking-water, since, not expecting to stop, we had come out unprovided. Brown it was who saved the methylated spirit from upsetting, and

Brown was rewarded presently with an excellent cup of tea, into which Miss Randolph had dropped two lumps of sugar with her own blessed little pink-tipped fingers. As a matter of fact, in ordinary circumstances sugar in tea is medicinal to my taste; but when that angel sat with a lump between her fingers asking how many I would have, though she had just let Jimmy Sherlock put in his own, I would have said half a dozen, if that would have left any over for her. And if the taste was medicinal, why, it had a curative effect on my injured feelings.

Refreshed, invigorated by more than tea, I felt ready for anything. Darkness was falling, but I didn't light the lamps. The road was empty, a torch of dusky red blazing along the west. We started, going cautiously; our tongues silent, our eyes alert. By-and-by, from afar off, we caught the twinkle of low-set, yellow lights. We were coming to the neighbourhood of the *octroi*. Luckily it was cold; the door and windows of the house would certainly be shut, unless the men were engaged in transacting business in the road. I now hurriedly explained to Miss Randolph the exact method I meant to adopt, and the word was passed round to be "mum." While the tea-things were being packed away, a short time ago, I had well oiled the wheels and chains; the car moved as silently as a bat, except for the chuff! chuff! of the motor. About a hundred yards from the lights I put on speed, and when we had begun to scud along like a ship with all sails set, I took out the clutch and let the motor run free. By this time we were within thirty yards of a building which I

now felt certain was the *octroi*. The car, which had
been going extremely fast, dashed on, coasting past
the little lighted house by its own impetus. Not a
sound, not a creak of a wheel, not the grating of a
chain.

On we sped for full forty yards past the *octroi*
before we lost speed, and I had to slip in the clutch.

"Oh, *Brown!*" breathed my Goddess ecstatically.
Just that, and no more. But if I had been Jack
Winston and asked her to marry me at this moment,
I believe she would have said "yes," in sheer exuber-
ance of grateful bliss.

So far, so good, but we were not yet out of the
wood. We drove quietly on into the town, expecting
every moment to be challenged for not lighting our
lamps, though we were within our rights, really, dark
as it was, for it was not yet an hour after sunset.
But nothing happened; not even a dog barked. We
crossed the high bridge spanning the Aude, and the
old *cité*, which we had come to see, loomed black
against the dusky sky. No one molested us; no
fiery *gendarme* leaped from the shadows commanding
us to stop. My small trumps were taking all the
tricks, but I had a big one still in my hand. We
were now—having crossed the bridge and left the new
town behind us—in a comparatively deserted region.

"My idea," I said quietly to Miss Randolph, "is to
drive the car into some dark, back street, far from the
ken of the *gendarme*. It is six o'clock. People are
sitting down to dinner. That is in our favour.
I shall, if possible, find a place where the car may
stand for several hours without being remarked,

while your visit is paid to the *cité*. Here, now, is
the very place!" I broke short my disquisition to
remark; for as I elaborated my plan, driving very
slowly, we had arrived before a dingy mews with
a waggon standing, shafts down, on the cobbles.
I turned in and stopped both car and motor.

"This shelter might have been made for us," I said,
beginning to find a good deal of pleasure in the
situation. "The only difficulty is" (out with my
big trump) "that of course someone must stay with
the car. It is my place, miss, to do so. But, unfortunately, it is after hours for showing the ramparts, the
interior of the towers, the dungeons, and so on, which
are really the attractions of the wonderful, old restored
mediæval city. I have been here before. I know
the *gardien*, and might, if I were in the party, induce
him to make an exception in your favour. Still, as
it is, the best I can do will be to write a note and ask
him to take you through."

Jimmy laughed, or I should say, chortled. "I should
think a *banknote* would appeal to the *gardien's* intelligence better than any other kind," said he, "and
I will see that he gets it."

"I advise you not to do that, sir," I remarked
quietly. "The *gardien* here isn't that sort of man
at all. He would be mortally offended if you tried
to bribe him, and would certainly refuse to do anything for you."

"I'm sure a letter would be of very little use," said
Miss Randolph. "I think we must manage to have
you with us somehow, Brown. Couldn't we hire
a man to look after the car?"

"I shouldn't like to take the risk," said I. "And remember, miss, we are in hiding."

"*I* don't want to see the old thing," protested Aunt Mary. "I've gone through so much to-day I feel a thousand years old. I'm not going to climb any hills or see any sights. I want my dinner."

"I think we'd better get on," advised Sherlock. "Not much fun poking about in a lot of old ruins in the dark."

"They're not ruins, and it isn't dark," said Miss Randolph. "Look at the sky! The moon's coming up this minute. If you don't want to see the *cité*, Jimmy, you might just as well sit here in the car while the rest of us go."

"I shall sit with him," announced Aunt Mary. "And if you *must* go on this wild goose chase, do for pity's sake hurry back, or we shall be frozen."

I began to fear that the scheme would fall through, with so much against it, but Miss Randolph kept to her resolution despite the moving picture of her relative's suffering.

"Oh yes, we will hurry back. We shan't be long," she said cheerfully, "we " meaning herself and her courier *mécanicien*. "You can't be cold in your furs; it's very early yet; you had a good tea; and Brown and I will whisk you off to some dear little village inn in time for an eight o'clock dinner."

I knew we should do nothing of the kind, but mine not to reason why, mine but to do or die—with her.

I daresay, my dear Montie, that even to you "Carcassonne" expresses nothing in particular. To those who have been there the name must, I think, always bring with it an imperishable recollection. Carcassonne is one of the unique places of the world. Years ago—as far back as the Romans, probably much further—there was a fortress on this hill, which commanded one of the chief roads into Spain. Afterwards it was used by the Visigoths, and in the Middle Ages it reached its highest importance under St. Louis. Then gradually it sank again into insignificance, and early last century there was a proposal that the ruins should be destroyed. By this time hardly anyone lived in the old city on the hill, a new and flourishing modern town (laid out in parallelograms) having sprung up in the plain. The demolition of the ancient ruins was prevented by one Cros-Mayrevieille, a native of Carcassonne, who succeeded in whipping up such enthusiasm on behalf of his birthplace that the city was made into a *monument historique*, and money was granted for its complete reconstruction by Viollet le Duc. A large sum has been spent, great works have been carried out, and the result is one of the most extraordinary feats of restoration in the history of the world.

From afar off this city upon a hill makes a vivid appeal to the imagination. Its great assemblage of towers, walls, and battlements, rising clear-cut and majestic against the sky, suggests at the first glimpse one of those imaginary mediæval cities that Doré loved to draw as illustrations to the *Contes Drolatiques*. So extraordinary is the apparition of this ancient, silent, fortified city existing in the midst of the railway epoch that one is tempted to think it a mirage, some strange trick of the senses, which, on rubbing the eyes, must disappear. And the nearer one draws, the more vivid does this impression become. Everything perfect, marvellously perfect, yet with no jarring hint of newness. It is well-nigh impossible at any time to tell where the original structure ends and where Viollet le Duc's restoration begins, and on what a grand scale it all is.

By moonlight the effect was really glorious. My Goddess and I walked over a drawbridge and entered the silent, grass-grown streets of the old, old city, where quaint and ancient houses, given up now to the poor, huddle under the protecting walls of the great fortress. We were in a perfect mediæval city, just as it existed in the time of the Crusades. In thus exactly realising the life of a garrisoned fortress of those stirring days, I found much the same dramatic interest I feel on stepping into the silent streets of Pompeii, where the ghosts seem more real than I.

We stopped at the house of the _gardien_, and I made an excuse for leaving Miss Randolph at a little distance, as I talked to him, reminded him of my last visit, and begged that, as a favour, he would show us about, although it was now "after hours." He is a very good fellow, courteous and intelligent, speaking with the noticeably distinct enunciation which seems to be the mark of all these guardians of _monuments historiques_ in France; and when he understood that there was a lady in the case, he readily consented to oblige, though I suspect he left his supper in the midst. He took off his cap to

Miss Randolph's beauty, etherealised by the moon's magic, and we all three started on our expedition. We were conducted into huge, round towers and out upon lofty, commanding battlements, whence we could gaze through a haze of moonlight over a great sweep of country, with here and there the sparkle of a winding river, like a diamond necklace flung down carelessly on a purple cushion. Our guide conscientiously pointed out the stations of the sentries and the guards, the disposition of the towers for mutual defence (each a bowshot from the other), the sally-ports, the secret passages communicating with underground tunnels for revictualling the city in time of siege; and so realistic were our surroundings that I fancied Miss Randolph once or twice actually caught herself listening in vain for the tramp of mailed feet, the hoarse word of command. At all events, I'm sure she forgot for the time being all about Aunt Mary and Jimmy Payne waiting in the car, and I didn't think it incumbent upon me to remind her of their existence or necessities. We lingered long enough in the splendid region of towers, battlements, and ramparts to do them full justice. Then, when I had slipped something of no importance into the *gardien's* hand, we reluctantly departed, often looking back as we went down the hill. As we left the old city we did not leave it alone. A group of young men and women of a humble class were hurrying down just before us on their way to the new town. We were so near that we couldn't help overhearing their eager talk of a spectacle they were on their way to see, and judging from the fragments we caught, this was to be a kind of Passion Play. Although I had been at Carcassonne before, I didn't know that such a thing existed in France, or, indeed, outside Oberammergau and a few villages in the Tyrol. Miss Randolph questioned me about it, but I could tell her nothing, and she exclaimed rather shamefacedly, "Oh, *how* I should love to go!"

"Would you let me take you there, just to look on for a few minutes, miss?" I doubtfully asked.

"I should like it above anything," said she. "Only —we've already kept those poor people waiting too long, I'm afraid."

"This needn't keep them very much longer," said I, "and it may be the last chance you will ever have of seeing such a thing."

"Oh, well, I can't resist," she cried. "We'll go— and I'll take the scolding afterwards."

We did go, following our leaders until we came to a good-sized booth with a crowd round it. The admission was twopence each, but the best seats cost a franc. We went in and found ourselves in a long, canvas room, with sloping seats and a small stage at one end lighted by oil lamps.

The place was dreadfully hot, and smelled strongly of humanity. Presently a bell rang; there was solemn music on a tinkling piano and a young actor, bare-faced and dressed in a white classical dress, took his place near the stage, beginning to recite in a clear, sympathetic voice. He was the choragus, explaining to us what was to happen in the play. The curtain went up, to reveal a tableau of Adam and Eve in very palpable flesh tights, with garlands of fig leaves festooned about their bodies.

Adam, with an elaborate false beard, slept under a tree. Then to the accompaniment of the choragus' explanation a mechanical snake appeared in the branches with an apple in its mouth. An unseen person off the stage made the snake twist and writhe. Eve put out her hand, took the apple, and ate a bit. Adam waking, she pointed to the tree and to the fruit, offering him a piece. He demurred in pantomime, but accepted and swallowed what was left of the apple. Instantly there appeared at the wing an angel with a long, flaxen wig, who threatened the guilty pair with a tinsel sword. They cowered, and then shading their eyes with their hands, were walking sadly away when the curtain fell. It was tableau number one, showing the fall of man.

The audience on the whole received the exhibition with devotional reverence, but a knot of young men openly tittered and jeered, commenting satirically upon the deficiencies in the stage management. Then, with more music, began the scenes from the New Testament. One was rather pretty, introducing the woman at the well, Christ being impersonated by a sweet-faced young man in white, with a light brown wig and beard. The girl who played the Virgin was not more than twenty, and had a serene prettiness, with an air of grave modesty, which were very attractive. She wore her own long hair falling like a mantle over her dark dress as far down as the knees.

Each scene lasted perhaps five minutes, the characters on the stage speaking no word, but opening

their mouths and moving their bodies in time with
the recitation of the choragus. We had the betrayal
in the garden, the trial before Pilate, the scourging,
the crucifixion, and the resurrection, all given with
feeling and surprising dignity, and in the crucifixion
scene, with pathos. Most of the women in the
audience were in tears, their compassion spending
itself noticeably more upon the Virgin's sorrow than
upon her Son's agony; and all through the repre-
sentation the same irreverent knot of scoffers continued to laugh, to whistle, to mimic. From many
parts of the tent there were indignant cries of
"Shame!" and "Silence!" but the disturbers went
on to the end, quite regardless of good taste and the
pious feelings of the majority.

I heard whispers which informed us that this
company of players had no repertoire; such a thing
they would have considered sacrilegious, but they
travelled all over France in caravans, carrying their
own scenery and costumes. We dared not stay till
the very end of the performance, but had to get up
and steal quietly out, with Aunt Mary heavy on our
consciences.

I believe poor little Miss Randolph really was
afraid of that scolding she had prophesied. But
behold, vice was its own reward, and the enemy was
delivered into our hands. We arrived at the mews,
and there was the car; but there was not Aunt Mary
nor yet Sherlock-Fauntleroy. In their place, curled
up in the *tonneau*, reclined a callow French youth,
comfortably snoozing, with his coat-collar turned up
to his ears. We roused him, learned that he had

been caught *en passant* and hired at the rate of two
francs an hour to await the return of a lady and
gentleman; also that he had been in his present
position for nearly an hour. One lady and gentleman seemed to his mind as good as another, for when
offered a five-franc piece he showed no hesitation in
delivering up his charge to us, although, for all he
could tell, we might have been the rankest of rank
impostors. After the departure of this faithless
guardian, Miss Randolph and I sat enthroned in the
car for some twenty minutes before Aunt Mary and
Jimmy came speeding round the corner of the mews.
They brought with them an atmosphere of warmth
and good cheer, and at first sniff it was evident that
they had dined where dining in both solid and liquid
branches was a fine art.

In my part of servant I was not "on" in the
ensuing comedy; but I listened "in the wings," and
chuckled inwardly. Well did Miss Randolph fill the
rôle of injured virtue which she had taken up at such
short notice. Her surprise that Aunt Mary and
Jimmy could have been capable of betraying her
trust in them, that they should have gone off and
left a valuable car, which wasn't even hers, to the
tender mercies of a stupid little boy, a perfect
stranger, was bravely done. It was represented as
a miracle that the Napier and everything in it had
not been stolen during their absence; and the good
dinner the culprits had enjoyed at the neighbouring
hotel could not fortify them against the blighting
sense of their own depravity so vividly brought home.

Not a reproach for us; all the wind had been taken

out of their sails.   A sadder and wiser Jimmy and
Aunt Mary meekly allowed themselves to be driven
on through the cold moonlight, with distant gleams
of towered towns, to Narbonne, where I am writing
to you, after having dined and cleaned the car.
Our hotel is not an ideal one; yet on my hard pillow
my head, I ween, will lie easier than on a downy one
last night.   We arrived late, and will leave early,
to lessen the chances of being pounced upon by the
clutches of the law.   But I begin to hope that, after
all, those peasants decided to let well alone, and that
we shall escape scatheless.

When I was a little boy we used to have honey
in red-brown earthenware pots labelled ''Finest
Narbonne Honey,'' and for years the place figured
in my imagination as a smiling region of brilliant
flowers.   But the disillusioning reality is a dusty,
rather noisy, very commercial town, paved with
stones the most abominable; and between Carcassonne and here the roads grow more abominable
with every kilometre.   I am tired, but not unhappy;
and so, good night.

Your fraudulent friend,
                    BROWN-WINSTON.

JACK WINSTON TO LORD LANE

HOTEL DU LOUVRE, MARSEILLES,
December 18.

My dear Montie,

We have just been passing through some of
the most interesting parts of France, therefore in the
world, and I have derived a certain rarefied enjoyment from it all, as I should have been only half a
man not to do. But Brown stock has gone down a
little since Carcassonne, why, I know not, though I
suspect; and there is depression, if not panic in the
market. Jimmy, having made his peace and promised caution, has again been promoted to the post of
driver, and from the Jehu point of view I must
confess that during a large part of the journey he
has covered himself with as much credit as dust.
This is saying a good deal, for, owing to the slight
rainfalls in these southern departments, the roads are
often buried inches deep under a coating of grey,
pungent dust, enveloping all passing vehicles in a
noisome cloud. They have also, set in their surface
at irregular intervals, large pans or dishes with perpendicular walls from an inch to three inches in
depth. These dishes being concealed by the all-
pervading dust, it is impossible—at least for a Jimmy

Payne—to know where they are until the wheels bump into them. Sometimes one of our wheels would drop in, sometimes all four. You may imagine the strain of this sort of work upon the tyres, frame, and springs. But in a whole day's run of a hundred and thirty miles we punctured only one tyre, which I mended in fifteen minutes.

Béziers, seen from a distance, set strikingly upon a hill, looked an imposing town, but turned out to be an ordinary and dirty place when we came to ascend its long, winding streets. Beyond, we ran for a while along the edge of a great lagoon, and knew, though we could not see it, that the Mediterranean lay close at our right hand.

At Montpellier we did not stop, and I delivered no lecture on the subject of the gorgeous, all-conquering Duchess, as I might have been tempted to do if we'd had no addition to our party. It's a large, bright, and stately town, very liveable-looking; but nothing was said about lingering, though there are some things worth seeing. We had an impressive entrance into the ancient city of Nîmes, running in by early moonlight, across a great, open plain, under a spacious, purpling dome of sky, the sun dying in carmine behind us, the evening star a big, flashing diamond in the moon-paled east. The old Roman amphitheatre stood up darkly and nobly in the silver twilight; but we passed on to our hotel, the programme evidently being to satisfy the senses at the expense of the soul. They do one very well at the hotel in Nîmes, but I looked forward hopefully to a request to play courier among the sights of the dear

old town next morning. It did not come, however.
The two ladies went forth with Jimmy, and as I saw
them go I could but acknowledge my rival to be a
personable fellow. Sherlock Holmes and Little Lord
Fauntleroy were both personable fellows in their
way, and it is useless to deny Jimmy's possession of
the picked attributes of each.

For some reason the word seems to have gone
forth that we are to hurry on to Cannes. In the
circumstances I am inclined to change my mind,
and instead of wishing my dear mother to have
departed before our arrival, I'm not sure it wouldn't
be wiser to hope that she'll still be there. Miss
Randolph "hasn't decided what she'll do after reaching the Riviera." I can't help feeling that Jimmy
Sherlock has succeeded in getting in some deadly
work of a mysterious nature. It's on the cards that
I may find at Cannes or Nice that the trip is finished, and Brown is finished too. Then, as I can't
and won't part from my Goddess without a Titanic
struggle, I might find it convenient to tell my mother
all, throw myself on her mercy, and get her to inter-
cede with Miss Randolph for me. You may argue
that her views regarding the fair Barrow are likely to
militate against co-operation in this new direction;
but I can be eloquent on occasion, and even a mother
must see that a Barrow is nothing beside a Goddess.

Altogether, I am nervous. The future looks
wobbly, and it is not a pleasant sensation to feel
that one is being secretly undermined. Jimmy had
better look out, though. The first shadow of proof
I get that he's breaking his half of the bargain he

shall learn that even a *chauffeur* will turn. And I look upon Cannes, somehow, as the turning-point in more senses of the word than one.

But to our muttons. No pleasant dallying for me in beautiful old Nîmes or Arles, either one of which would repay weeks of lingering. What dallying there was, Jimmy got — confound him! — and my only joy was in his hatred of early rising. They had him up at an unearthly hour for a glimpse of the amphitheatre and the Maison Carrée at Nîmes, and by nine we were on the road to Arles, Payne driving with creditable caution. We crossed the Rhone and completed the eighteen flat miles in little more than thirty minutes. When we arrived at the end of this time in the astonishing little town of Arles, halting in a diminutive square with two great pillars of granite and a superb Corinthian pediment (dating from Roman occupation) built into the walls of modern houses, Miss Randolph announced that they would walk about for half an hour and look at the antiquities. "Half an hour!" I couldn't help echoing; "why, Arles is one of the most interesting places in France. It is an open-air museum."

"I know," said she, looking up at me with an odd expression which I would have given many a bright sovereign for the skill to read. "But maybe I shall have a chance to see it some other time, and the others don't care much for antiquities or architecture. We really *must* hurry as fast as possible to Cannes."

Now, why—why? What is to happen at Cannes? Is Jimmy's loathly hand in this? Or — blessed thought!—is all sight-seeing for her, as well as for me, poisoned by his society? Is she regretting her rash generosity in promising to carry him to the Riviera (to say nothing of *Lord Lane!*) and is she panting to rid herself of him? I daren't hope it. But write me your deduction. Perhaps in your enforced inaction at Davos it may amuse you to piece together a theory and account for the actions of certain persons in France, whom possibly you know better than if you had ever met them.

While the three went off to bolt in one bite such delicate morsels as the sculptured porch of the cathedral of St. Trophinus and the Roman theatre I gloomily played Casabianca by the car, Ixion at the wheel, or what you will. I waited their return before the hotel, and no sooner did they come back, at the end of their stingy half-hour, than we started, taking the road across the great plain of La Crau towards Salon.

A most extraordinary region that plain of La Crau. It is as flat as a pancake, only far away to the north one sees a range of brown, stony mountains. Formerly it was a forbidding, stony desert, the dumping-place for every pebble and boulder brought down by the Rhone and the Durance. But all over the vast wilderness there has been carried out a wonderful system of irrigation, and now it yields sweet herbage for sheep, while figs, mulberries, and cypresses are dotted in green oases. The surface of the land is thickly veined with the beneficent little canals, carrying life-giving water from the Canal de Craponne, which has its origin at La Roque, on the Durance.

Across this vast plain we raced towards Salon, along a road straight as if drawn by a ruler, and bordered by small poplars standing shoulder to shoulder like trees in a child's box of toys. We met no other vehicles; we seemed to have the world to ourselves; but once, far along the road, we spied a black dot which seemed to come towards us with incredible speed, growing larger as it came. In less time than it takes to write we saw that it was an enormous racing automobile, probably undergoing a test of speed. We were running at our own highest pace, perhaps forty-five miles an hour; the thing approaching us was coming at seventy or more. You may imagine the rush of air as we passed each other. One glimpse we had of a masked automobilist like a figure of death in an Albert Dürer cartoon, or the familiar of a Vehmgericht, and then we were gasping in the vortex of air caused by the speed of the gigantic car. Almost before we could turn our heads it was a black dot again on the horizon. Perhaps it was the great Fournier himself.

Beyond Salon the road becomes interestingly *accidentée*. One climbs among the mountains which fold Marseilles in their encircling arms, and has spacious views over the great Etang de Berre to the glittering Mediterranean. The Napier crested the hills without faltering, and from the top we had a long run down (over bad *pavé* at the last) into the lively, noisy streets of gay Marseilles, Payne guiding the car very decently over intricate tram lines, finally turning across the pavement to circle into the white, airy court of a large hotel. When my passengers had got down I drove the car to a *garage* and went quietly off to another hotel, where, warned by past experience at Pau, I entered myself in the register modestly as James Brown.

Now I shall hurl at your devoted and friendly head this enormous letter, and presently shall begin another to tell of the Further Adventures on the Riviera of

Your much-enduring Friend,
The AMATEUR CHAUFFEUR.

MOLLY RANDOLPH TO HER FATHER

GRAND HOTEL, TOULON,
December 20.

My Wingless Angel,

It's lucky your poor dear hair is getting conspicuous by its absence, or it would stand up on
end, I don't doubt, when you read a few lines farther.
So, you see, even baldness is a blessing in disguise.

I won't keep you in suspense. The worst shall
come first; after all that's happened I don't mind
such a little thing as an anticlimax in writing to my
indulgent and uncritical Dad.

Now for it.

I have deserted Aunt Mary and Jimmy Payne in
a gorge. I am alone in a hotel—with Brown. Yet
I ask you to suspend judgment; I have not exactly
eloped.

It is all Jimmy Payne's fault.

I wired you yesterday from Marseilles, because
I hadn't written since my second letter from Pau,
when I told you how Aunt Mary had persuaded me
that it would be perfectly caddish not to invite
Jimmy to drive with us to the Riviera, as his car
was there and he was going that way. I felt in my
bones to an almost rheumatic extent that to ask him
would be a big mistake; still, in a weak moment I

consented, when Jimmy had been particularly nice
and had just paid you a whole heap of compliments.
I lay awake nearly all night afterwards, thinking
whether 'twere nobler in the mind of Molly to hurt
Brown's feelings or Jimmy's, since injury must be
dealt to one.   Finally, I tossed up for it in the sanctity
of my chamber.   Heads, Brown drives; tails, Jimmy;
and it was tails.   Well, I'd vowed that should settle
it, so I wouldn't go back on myself; and, anyhow,
Jimmy was the guest, so that French copper had the
rights of it.   I did my best to make all straight with
the Lightning Conductor, who behaved like the trump
he is.

Jimmy had spared no pains or expense in advertising himself as an expert driver, nevertheless I
knew him well enough not to be surprised at finding
out he didn't know much more than I did.   I soon
saw that, though the first day everything went well
enough.   The second day he nearly landed us in a
dreadful scrape with some peasants, but since Brown
brought us safely through, I won't tell tales out of
school, especially as the tables were rather turned
on the poor fellow at Carcassonne—the most splendid
place.   I send you with this a little book all about it,
full of pictures, and you are to be sure to read it.
I was rather sorry for Jimmy afterwards; he was
so humble, and besides, he took a cold in his head
waiting in the car while I went sight-seeing.   He
promised to be very prudent if I would only trust
him again, and cleverly took my mind off his late
misdeeds by exciting my curiosity.   At breakfast
in Narbonne, where we'd unexpectedly stayed the

night, he hinted darkly of most exciting events in which we were intimately concerned, which would in all probability take place at Cannes, if we could only arrive there soon enough. I couldn't get him to tell me what they were, but I fancy Aunt Mary is at least partly in his confidence. She wouldn't betray him, but she assured me that to miss the treat in store for us would mean lasting regret. And she was bursting with importance and mystery. Now I don't believe much in Jimmy's show; nothing of his ever does come off, except his hat when he drives. Still, a little of Jimmy's society goes a long way in the intimate association of a motoring journey; what it *would* be in married life I don't know and don't want to know; and as I too began to think I shouldn't be sorry to get to the Riviera, I consented to be whirled through some lovely places, just to satisfy Aunt Mary and Jimmy's craving for haste, and lack of love for ancient architecture.

We arrived at Marseilles, Jimmy doing well. I *would* see something of the place, for I was true to my Monte Cristo, and insisted upon having a glimpse of the Château d'If. We got in at night, and stayed at a delightful hotel. Early in the morning I was up, and rather than I should take Brown as courier, Jimmy (who resents Brown) was up early too. We had breakfast together—for Aunt Mary stayed in bed—and went out to walk. But it wasn't like going about with the Lightning Conductor, who knows everything and has been everywhere before. We had to inquire our way every minute, and shouldn't have known which things were worth seeing if Monsieur Rathgeb, the landlord, hadn't told us to be sure and go up the hill of Notre Dame de la Garde for the view; so we went up in a lift, and it was glorious. Some soldiers marching on a green boulevard below looked like tiny black-beetles, and the music of their bugle band came floating faintly to us like sounds heard through a gramophone. The Ile d'If and all the others were splendid from there, and I would have liked to stay a long time, if Jimmy hadn't begun to be tiresome and harangue me about the confidential way in which I treat Brown. "Social distinctions," said he didactically, "are the bulwarks of society." Ha, ha! I couldn't help laughing—could you in my place? I told him I thought he would make a fortune as a lecturer, but lectures weren't much in my line; and I asked if he'd ever read Ibsen's *Pillars of Society*, which of course he hadn't. Then we went down in the lift, and back to the hotel for Aunt Mary, who naturally wanted to shop; and by the time she had finished buying veils and cold cream it was time for lunch, which we had in one of the most charming restaurants I was ever in, on the Corniche Road. I don't care so very much about good things to eat; but I do think that oysters, *langouste à l'Americaine*, *bouillabaisse à la Provençale*, perfectly cooked and served, and mixed with a heavenly view, may be something to rave about. Oh, there's a lot to see and do in Marseilles, I assure you, Dad, though one's friends never seem to tell you much about it; and it was three o'clock in the afternoon before I would consent to be torn away. Of course, so far south the daylight lingers long; still, we knew we had but an hour and a half more of it when we started. There had been a shower of rain while Aunt Mary and I were packing, and we had not been out of the hotel many minutes when we had a surprise.

Jimmy was driving along a paved street, slimy with fresh mud, and confusing with the dash and clash of electric street cars, which Jimmy is English enough to call "trams." He tried to pass one on the off side, but just as he was getting ahead of it another huge car came whizzing along from the opposite direction. I didn't say a word. I just "sat tight," but I had the queerest feeling in my feet as if I wanted to jump or do something. It looked as if we were going to be pinched right between the two, and I'd have given a good deal if Brown had been at the helm, for I would have been sure that somehow he'd contrive to get us through all right. But Jimmy lost his head—and indeed there are only a few men who wouldn't, for the drivers of both cars were furiously clanging their bells, and the whole world seemed to be nothing but noise, noise, and great moving things coming every way at once. He jammed on the brakes suddenly, which was just what Brown in the *tonneau* was trying to warn him not to do, and before I knew what had happened our automobile waltzed round on the road with a slippery sort of slide, the way your foot does when you step on ice under snow.

I thought we were finished, and I'm afraid I shut my eyes. "Just like a girl!" O yes, thank you; I know that; but I didn't know it or anything else at that minute. There was loud shouting and swearing, then a bump, a noise of splintering wood, another bump, and we were still alive and unhurt, with a buzz of voices round us—quite *unkind* voices some of them, though I never felt more as if I wanted kindness. It occurred to me to open my eyes, and I found that we had brought up against the curbstone, while one of our mud-guards had been smashed by the iron rail of the electric street car, now stationary. Our Napier had turned completely round. The conductor of the tram was scrutinising his scratched rail and saying things; but Brown, who had jumped out to examine into our damage, slyly slipped something that looked like a five-franc piece into his hand. This reminds me, I must pay Brown back; he can't refuse such a thing as that, though it seems he has taken a sort of pledge against accepting tips in his professional career. Funny, isn't it? "For a touch of new paint," I heard him murmur to the conductor in his nice French, and that man must have been in a great hurry to try the effect of the "touch," for no sooner did the coin change hands than he stopped scolding, and away buzzed the big electric bumble-bee.

"For *mercy's* sake, what was it that happened?" gasped Aunt Mary.

"Side-slip, miss," said Brown in a tone dry enough to turn the mud to dust, "from putting on the brakes too quickly. A driver can't be too careful on a surface like this." Which was one for Jimmy.

The poor fellow took it with outward meekness, though I saw his eyes give a flash—and, do you know, our blond Jimmy can look quite malevolent!

He didn't speak to Brown, but turned to me, and said the side-slip wasn't really his fault at all; it might happen to anybody in greasy weather; but he would be still more cautious now than before. I didn't like to humiliate a guest by superseding him with a servant, capable as the servant is, so I said that I hoped he *would* be very careful, and we started on again, somewhat chastened in our mood, driving slowly, slowly, through interminable suburbs to a place called Aubagne.

There was a splendid sunset after the rain, with a wonderful effect of heavy violet cloud-curtains with jagged gold edges, drawn up to show a clear sky of pale beryl-green; and sharp against the green were cut out purple mountains and white villages that looked like flocks of resting gulls. We were in wild and beautiful country by the time the thickening clouds compelled us to stop and light our two oil-lamps and the huge acetylene Bleriot.

There was a good deal of wind, and Aunt Mary began to shiver as we started on, still going slowly. "Oh dear!" she exclaimed crossly, "we shall never get anywhere to-night if we crawl like this. Surely there's no danger now?"

That was enough for Jimmy. He said that certainly there was no danger now, and never had been. Opening the throttle, he began to tell me anecdotes of a trip he had made with his Panhard over the Stelvio with snow on the ground. If I weren't afraid now of a decent pace, he'd get us into Toulon in no time.

I do hate to have people think I'm afraid, so of

course I denied it sharply, and we began to fly down hill. Our lamps seemed to have shut the night down closely all around us. We didn't see much except the road with the light flying along it; but suddenly, circling round a curve, there appeared—dark within the brilliant circle of our Bleriot—a great, unlighted waggon lumbering up the hill we were descending, and on the wrong side of the road.

We were close on to it, and oh, Dad, that was a bad moment! It was made up of lightning-quick impressions and feelings, no reasoning at all. Jimmy was frantically blowing the horn, though it was too late to be of much good. I had a vision of a startled Jack-in-the-box man appearing from the bottom of the waggon to snatch wildly at the reins; the next instant our car waltzed round just as it had in Marseilles, twisted off the road, and, with a loud shriek from Aunt Mary, who had clutched me by the arm, we all pitched headlong into darkness.

It felt as if we were falling for ever so long, just as it does in a dream before you wake up with a great start; but I suppose it really wasn't more than a second. The next thing I knew, I was on my hands and knees among some stones; and evidently I'm vainer than I fancied, for among other thoughts coming one on top of the other, I was glad my *face* wasn't hurt. I've always imagined that it must be terrible for a girl to come to herself after an accident and find she had no face.

I scrambled to my feet and began calling to the others. I think I called Brown first, because, you see, he is so quick in emergencies, and he would be ready to look after the others. But he didn't speak, and the most awful cold, sick feeling settled down on my heart. "Oh, Brown, Brown!" I heard myself crying, just as you hear yourself in a nightmare, and it hardly seemed more real than that. Into the midst of my calling Aunt Mary's voice mingled, and I was thankful, for it didn't sound as if she were much hurt.

Our lamps had gone out, and it was almost pitch dark now, for clouds covered the moon. But there came a glimmer, which kept growing brighter; and looking up I saw a man standing with a lantern held over his head, peering down a steep bank with a look of horror. The same glimmer showed me something else—Brown's face on the ground, white as a stone, his eyes wide open with an unseeing stare. I ran to him, and found that I was pushing Aunt Mary back, as she was trying to get up from somewhere close at hand. She caught at me, and wouldn't let me go by. "Oh dear, oh dear!" she was sobbing, and I begged her to tell me if she were hurt.

"No, thank Heaven! I fell on Brown," she said, "and that saved me."

I could have boxed her ears. One would have thought, to hear her, that he was a sort of fire-escape. I snatched my dress out of her hands, and knelt down beside poor Brown, who was perhaps dead, all through my fault—for I saw now that I ought never to have let Jimmy Payne drive the car. By this time the man with the lantern (it was the carter who had made the trouble for us) had slid down the steep bank, and come straight to where I was kneeling.

"*Ah, mademoiselle, il est mort!*" he exclaimed. How I did hate him! I screamed out, "He isn't, he isn't!" but it was only to make myself believe it wasn't true, and I couldn't help crying — big hot tears that splashed right down into Brown's eyes. And I suppose it was their being so hot that woke him up, for he did wake up, and looked straight at me, dazed at first, then sensibly—such a queer effect, the intelligence and brightness taking the place of that frightened stare. The first thing he said was, "Are you hurt?" And I said "No"; and then I discovered that I was holding his hand as fast as ever I could —only think, holding your *chauffeur's* hand!—but such a brave, faithful *chauffeur*, never thinking of his own face, as I had of mine, but of *me*.

That made me laugh and draw back, and we both said something about being glad. And I wanted to help him, but he didn't need any help, and was up like an arrow the next second. And then, for the first time, I saw the car, standing upright with Jimmy Payne, sitting in it, hanging on like grim death to the steering-post, which he was embracing as if he were a monkey on a stick.

I *did* laugh at that—one does laugh more when something dreadful has nearly happened, but not quite, than at any other time, I think—though into the midst of my laugh came a sudden little pain. It was in my left wrist, and it ached hard, one quick throb after another, as if they were in a hurry to get their chance to hurt. But I didn't say anything, for it seemed such a trifle. Brown assured me that he was "right as rain," that he'd only been dazed and perhaps unconscious for a minute through falling on his head. I wondered if he knew about Aunt Mary. But it was too delicate a subject to raise. Anyway, she hadn't a bruise. And wasn't it extraordinary about Jimmy? The car had "fallen on its feet," so to speak, and he had hung on to the steering-post so hard that not only had he kept his seat, but he had wrenched the steering-gear. Brown discovered this in peering into the works by the light of one of our own oil-lamps, relit from the carter's lantern. If the Napier hadn't been a magnificent car it would have been frightfully damaged, although, finding itself compelled to take a twelve-foot jump off the road, it had cleverly chosen comparatively smooth, meadow-like ground to descend upon. Not even a tyre was punctured; no harm whatever appeared to have been done except that, as I said, owing to Jimmy's savage contortions in search of safety, the steering-gear was wrenched.

There's a thing called a worm in steering-gear, it seems, also a rod; and new ones would have to be fitted in ours before we could go on again. When I heard this I felt rather qualmish, for my wrist was aching a good deal, and had begun to swell. Brown and the carter were talking together, and according to them the best thing seemed to be to carry luggage and rugs to the nearest village, Le Beausset, and try to get accommodation there for the night. Brown would go on to Toulon, he said, and try to get new parts for the car, with which he'd come back early in the morning.

Still I didn't say anything about my wrist. Aunt

Mary and I scrambled up the bank, and Brown, Jimmy, and the carter went back and forth for our things. The latter had been going away from Le Beausset, not towards it when the accident happened, but he agreed to turn round and take our luggage on his cart to the village. He made room for Aunt Mary too, sitting on bags and portmanteaus like Marius on the ruins of Carthage, and the rest of us walked, about a mile.

Le Beausset proved to be a tiny place, and at the solitary inn there was but one small bedroom to let, the rest being taken by some rough, selfish-looking commercial travellers, who were having an early dinner in a hot and smelly *salle à manger*, with every breath of air religiously excluded.

I thought that without being fussy I might draw the general attention to myself. I announced a wrist, and demanded a surgeon lest I had cracked a bone. Brown vanished like a pantomine demon, but returned almost immediately with a long face, and the intelligence that Le Beausset had neither surgeon nor resident doctor. There was no vehicle, not even a bicycle, to be had for love or money at this time of day, but he would make all haste to Toulon and send back a competent man. The worst of it was there might be delay, as it was about ten miles to Toulon. Halfway between Le Beausset and the big town was a small one called Ollioules, and there, it appeared, one could take an electric tram into Toulon; but it was a long way for a doctor to come, and it might be several hours before he could arrive.

"Then I'll go to Toulon with you," said I. "I

don't feel as if I could stand much waiting; the walk will take my mind off the pain, and I can have my wrist attended to the minute I get there."

Instantly Aunt Mary burst into a cataract of objections, and I only dammed the flood (quite in the proper sense of the word, because, like Marjorie Fleming, I was "most unusual calm; I did not give a single damn") by suggesting that, once in Toulon, I might send back a comfortable carriage and engage rooms in a good hotel for us all for the night.

"Well, I can't and won't stay here alone, that's flat," pronounced my dear aunt; and despite all her lectures against "liberty, fraternity, and equality" in my treatment of poor Brown, she was willing to let me go unchaperoned save by him, for the sake of retaining Jimmy Payne's protecting presence herself. As for Jimmy, it was easy to see that he didn't like the idea at all; but he had jarred himself a good deal in his eccentric fall, and evidently funked another tramp. He had limped ostentatiously every step of the way to Le Beausset. Brown was afraid that I wasn't up to the walk, but I assured him it would be much less uncomfortable than indefinite waiting, and I think he saw by my face that I was right. After all our delay it was only half-past five when we set off, and would scarcely have been thoroughly dark if it hadn't been for the clouds which had been boiling up from the west all over the sky.

I had no idea what kind of a walk we were in for when we started, neither had Brown, for he had never been over exactly this part of the world either walking or driving, but only in the train. We hadn't

been gone long when we plunged downwards into
a deep and winding mountain gorge, the kind of cut-
throat place where you'd expect brigands to grow on
blackberry bushes. Oh, but it was dark, with only
now and then a fitful gleam of moonlight cutting its
way through a rent in the inky clouds! Hardly had
the word "brigands" crept into my mind with an
accompaniment of heart-beats something like the
plink! plink! plink! villain entrance-music on the
stage, when two indistinct forms loomed out of the
blackness before us. A perpendicular wall of rock
shot up from the road on one side, and on the other,
in some unseen depth below, roared a torrent, which
drowned my voice when I whispered to Brown, so
I clutched his coat-sleeve instead of speaking.

The two men were chattering loudly in Italian.
"Ah, *Italian* brigands, worse and worse!" thought
I; but Brown said "Good-evening" to them boldly,
and they answered as mildly as a pair of lambs,
falling behind to let us pass on. I skipped along,
expecting at any instant to feel a knife in my back,
but the blade did not penetrate any part more vital
than my imagination, though the pair hung on our
footsteps till we emerged from the mountain defile
into the town of Ollioules.

I never knew what an attractive object an electric
tram could be, until I saw one there awaiting our
convenience, glittering with hospitable light. We
jumped in, and were flashed into Toulon in no time,
stopping close to the best hotel. We found that
they could accommodate our party, but Brown quite
took the upper hand; wouldn't allow me to stop and

talk, had me swept off to a very nice room, and said
that not only would he see about a surgeon for me,
but would arrange for a carriage to drive back for
Aunt Mary and Jimmy.

Till we got into the electric car at Ollioules I
hadn't noticed in the dark that Brown was carrying
anything. But he put down on the car seat quite a
heavy bag of mine and a sort of big dressing-case
of his own, which is his only baggage on the automobile. "Why *did* you lug all that?" I exclaimed.
"Oh, I thought you might need something before
the others arrived," said he, "and I didn't like to
trouble them to look after mine." Wasn't he thoughtful? And I was glad to have my bag — without
waiting. But just think of the state of that poor
fellow's muscles!

It was a quarter to seven when I got into my
rooms at the hotel, and ten minutes later the doctor
arrived. If he had had bad news to give me about
my wrist, I shouldn't have written the tale of this
adventure so frankly; but I can leave a good impression on your mind in the end by telling you that
all's well with your "one fair daughter." It's a sprain,
no worse; and the stuff which the clever man pre-
scribed has soothed the pain wonderfully. I'm so
thankful it's my left wrist, not the right; and so
ought you to be, or you would have to do without
letters. This is the time when I miss my maid; but
a dear little *femme de chambre* of the hotel helped
me dress, and it is wonderful how well you can get
on with only one hand.

Now I've something else to break to you, Dad.

The hotel was rather full, and all the private sitting-rooms were gone, otherwise I might have had dinner upstairs; but I drew the line at dining abjectly in a bedroom. Still, I didn't quite like the idea of sailing into a big *salle à manger*, alone, with a bound-up wrist, and perhaps making an exhibition of myself cutting up meat in a one-handed way. So before Brown went to call the doctor I just said to him casually that it would be an accommodation if he would dine in the *salle à manger* with me this once. He looked surprised, and seemed to hesitate a little before he said that he would do so with pleasure, if I thought it best. I was almost sorry I'd asked, but I wouldn't go back; and, anyhow, what else *could* I have done? He is extraordinarily gentlemanly in his looks and manner, and never takes the least advantage; so I hope you'll agree with me that of two evils I chose the less. And when I made the arrangement I supposed Aunt Mary and Jimmy would be arriving before bedtime, so that I should only be a lone, unprotected female for a few hours. But we hadn't been in the hotel five minutes before it came on to rain again, a perfect deluge this time, with thunder and lightning; and while the nice *femme de chambre* was helping me into a ducky little lace waist which was in the bag Brown had carried, to my great surprise a telegram was brought to my door. At first I thought there must be a mistake, but it really was for me. Brown had mentioned the name of the best hotel in Toulon, where we would try to get rooms before he and I left the others at Le Beausset; and the telegram was from Aunt Mary.

"Don't send carriage. Prefer stay here to driving in such storm. Feel sure you are safe without us."

I knew the carriage was already ordered, but thinking it might not have started, I scribbled a line in pencil to Brown, and enclosed the telegram. Aunt Mary is such a coward in thunderstorms; but it was silly of her, for it couldn't have gone on thundering all night. I was rather cross, but I had to laugh when I thought of Jimmy. He must have been wild.

If I'd known in time, perhaps I should have stayed ignominiously in my bedroom, but I wouldn't make a change then; it seemed such a tempest in a teapot. So when I was ready I went down as if nothing had happened, and looked around for Brown where I'd told him to meet me at half-past eight, in the hall. My goodness! I *was* surprised when I saw him in evening dress—a jolly dinner-jacket and a black tie. He might have been a prince. I wouldn't have said a word if I'd stopped to think; but I exclaimed on the impulse, and was dreadfully ashamed of myself, for he got rather red. He said quite humbly that he hadn't wished to discredit me, since I'd done him the honour of allowing him to serve me in a somewhat different capacity this evening (that was a nice way of putting it, wasn't it?), so he had decided to wear a suit of clothes which Mr. John Winston had left him; and he hoped I wasn't displeased.

After all, why should I have been when you come to think of it? So we dined at a little table all to ourselves, with pretty shaded candles and some lovely flowers. People were already beginning to leave the room, and nobody noticed anything strange about us as a couple; we appeared just like everybody else, only rather better looking, if I do say it myself. I had a very interesting talk with Brown, and he told me several things about his life, though I had to *draw* them out, as he is more modest than Jimmy Payne. He is far above his work, though he does it so well. I wish so much you could do something nice for him. Can't you?

This is the next morning, and I am writing in my room, waiting for the car to arrive. Aunt Mary and Jimmy will come in it; they've telegraphed again.

I am looking forward to the Riviera now, but I have such a queer, unsettled feeling—sort of half sad, without knowing why, which is stupid, as I'm having a splendid time. I suppose it's my wrist which has made me nervous.

Your loving
MOLLY.

FROM JACK WINSTON TO LORD LANE

GRAND HOTEL, TOULON,
December 19.

My good Montie,

It is getting on towards eleven o'clock at night, and as Payne has treated us to a smashup and I have walked some miles carrying I don't know how many pounds of luggage, you might think that I would be more inclined for bed than letter-writing. But, on the contrary, I have no desire for sleep. A change has come o'er my spirit. I am happy. I have dined alone with my Goddess. I almost took your advice and the opportunity to make a clean breast of things, but not quite. Presently I will tell you why, and ask if you don't think I was right in the circumstances.

The said circumstances I owe indirectly to Payne—also a lump on the back of my head; but that is a detail. I am in too blissful a frame of mind to-night to dwell on it or any other detail belonging to the accident, though maybe I'll give you the history of the affair in a future letter. Suffice it to say, before getting on to pleasanter things, that the car reposes in a lonesome meadow below a steep embankment about a dozen miles away, where it is perfectly safe till I can get back to its succour early to-morrow; Aunt Mary and Jimmy Sherlock are enjoying each other's society at a country inn rather nearer; Miss Randolph and I are here. She came on because she had to have a sprained wrist treated by a competent doctor; I came to buy new parts for the car; naturally we joined forces. The others were to have a carriage sent back to them from Toulon, but Aunt Mary funked the long drive on account of a furious storm. Miss Randolph could get no private sitting-room, and as, with a disabled wrist, she didn't care to face the ordeal of a *salle à manger* alone, she suggested that I should attend her at dinner. Not as a servant, mind, but "for this occasion only" as an equal.

For an instant I was doubtful, for her sake; but to have put a thought of impropriety into her sweet mind would have been coarse. Besides, the request from mistress to man was equivalent to a royal command. I hope, however, that had there been any fear of unfortunate consequences to her, I should have been strong enough to resist temptation.

I told her that, if she thought it best to condescend to my companionship, I should be highly honoured. And I added that I had with me a decent suit of black. We then parted; I went to find a doctor for Miss Randolph, and to see about a carriage to go back for the others to the village of Le Beausset. It also occurred to me that it would be nice to have a few flowers with which to deck the table for the happiest dinner of my life. The shops were not yet all closed, and at one not far from the hotel I selected some exquisite La France roses and a dozen sprays of forced white lilac, which I had once heard Miss Randolph say was among her favourite flowers. When I came to pay the bill, however—three francs a spray for the lilac, and a franc for each of the twelve roses—there were only a few coppers in my pocket. I remembered then that I had spent my last franc in Marseilles, without attaching any importance to the matter, as I'd wired for remittances to arrive at Cannes, and my "screw" due to-night would see me through till then. Now the situation was a bit awkward. I wanted to take the flowers with me and give them to the head waiter to place on the table where Miss Randolph and I would dine. I could not have them sent over and ask the hotel people to settle, because then they would appear on her bill to-morrow morning, as now she would certainly not pay my wages this evening. I couldn't bear to give up the bouquet; besides, I would need more ready money to-night. I had visions of ordering first-rate wine, and letting the Goddess suppose it was *vin compris* with the *table d'hôte* dinner. I therefore confessed my pennilessness to the shopman, and asked if I should be likely to find a *mont-de-piété* still open. He replied that the pawnshops did their busiest trade in the evening about this time, told me where I could find the best, and agreed to keep the flowers until my return.

The one thing of value I had with me was my monogrammed gold repeater, which my father gave me when I went up to Oxford, and I didn't much like parting with it, especially as I can't get it back

to-morrow, but will have to send back the ticket for
it from Cannes, when I'm in funds. However, I
had no choice, so I put my poor turnip up the spout,
and got a tenner for it. With this in French money
I retraced my steps to the florist's, and bore off my
fragrant spoils in triumph to the hotel. Hardly
had I given the flowers to the head waiter, ordered
an extra dish or two on the *menu* and a bottle of
Mumm to be iced, when a pencilled note from Miss
Randolph was handed to me. It contained a wire
from Aunt Mary, saying that she and Jimmy would
not leave their present quarters, on account of the
storm. I sent word to have the carriage stopped,
and luckily for the driver the message was just in
time. Then it struck me that in the circumstances
I had better put up at another hotel for the night.
I made all arrangements, had my bag taken over
to a little commercial sort of house near by, and
left myself just twenty minutes to bathe and change.
Gladstone could do it in five, I've been told. But
it was all I could manage in fifteen, for I had decided to do myself well, not to shame my dinner-
companion.

Thanks to my little trick of going to a different
hotel from the party when we are stopping anywhere
longer than one night, I can always indulge in
civilised garb of an evening therefore in the dressing-
case, which is my little all on the car, I carry something decent. Our mutual tailor, Montie, is not to
be despised; and when I'd got into my pumps and
all my things, I don't think there was much amiss.

I arrived at our rendezvous—the hall of the hotel

—just one minute before the appointed time; and five minutes later I saw Her coming downstairs.

I have sometimes caught a glimpse of her in the evenings, dressed for dinner at good hotels, and her frocks are like herself, always the most perfect. To-night she had no luggage except a bag I had carried, nevertheless she had somehow achieved a costume in which she was a vision. Perhaps if I were a woman I should have seen that she had on her day-skirt, with an evening bodice, but being merely a man over his ears in love, I can only tell you that the effect was dazzling. In admiration of her I forgot my own transformation until I saw her pretty eyebrows go up with surprise.

I felt my heart thump behind my rather jolly white waistcoat. On the second step from the bottom she stopped and exclaimed, "Why, Brown, how nice you look! You're exactly like a——" There she stopped, getting deliciously pink, as if she'd been a naughty child pinched by a "grown-up" in the midst of a malapropos remark. I could fill up the blank for myself, and was highly complimented by her opinion that I was "exactly like a gentleman." I explained that the clothes were Mr. Winston's, and had been donned with a highly laudable motive. It was evident that she approved both cause and effect; and we went in to dinner together.

I can't describe to you, my boy, the pure delight of that moment; the pride I felt in her beauty, the new and intoxicating sense of possession born of the *tête-à-tête*. But if you could have seen the lovely shadow her eyelashes made on her cheeks as she sat there opposite to me at our daintily appointed little table, you might partly understand.

Fortunately there was a small bunch of flowers on each table, so that ours was not conspicuous, save in superiority. She admired it, took out a spray of lilac and tucked it into the neck of her dress, the stem lying close against her white satin skin. Then, as she ate the *hors d'œuvres*, she sat silent and apparently thoughtful. It was not until we had begun with the soup that she spoke again.

"I do hope you won't think me rude or inquisitive, Brown," was her curiosity-provoking preface. "I don't mean to be either. But, you know, you interest me a good deal. In America we haven't precisely a middle class. It's all top and bottom with us, just like a tart with the inside forgotten. There, one wouldn't—wouldn't be apt to meet anyone quite like you. I—oh, I don't know how to put it. I'm afraid I began to say something that I can't finish. But—let me see, what *shall* I say? Isn't it a pity that with your intelligence and—and manners, and all you've learned, you can't get a position which would—would give you—er—better opportunities?"

At the moment I thought that no position could give me a better opportunity than I had; in fact, as I began to tell you in the first few lines of this letter, I was inclined to believe it sent by Providence as an unexpected way out of my difficulties. Here we were together in no danger of being disturbed by outsiders (one doesn't count a waiter); here was she in a benignant mood, interested in me, and inclined to kindness. In another second I would have blurted out the whole truth, when a voice seemed to say inside of me, "No, she is alone in this hotel to-night with you. She is, in a way, at your mercy. You will be doing an unchivalrous thing if, when she is practically deserted by her people and thrown upon your protection, you proclaim yourself a lover in place of a servant." That voice was right. Even you can't say it wasn't.

I swallowed my confession with a spoonful of soup, and nearly choked over the combination.

"The fact is," I said desperately yet cautiously, "since you are kind enough to take an interest, that I—cr—am not exactly what I seem to-day. My parents were gentlefolk, in a humble way." (I didn't go beyond the truth there, did I? And as for the "humble way," why, everything goes by comparison, from a king down to a mere viscount.) "They gave me an education" (they did, bless them!), "but owing to—er—strong pressure of circumstances" (the effect of Her beauty, seen in a Paris *garage*) "I decided to make use of my mechanical knowledge in the way I am doing at present."

"I suppose," commented my Goddess, with the sweetest sympathy, "that you had lost your money."

"Well," I said, thinking of my late penniless condition and my watch at the pawnshop, "I have a great deal less money now than I was brought up to expect."

"That is very sad," she sighed.

"And yet," I remarked, "it has its compensations. I consider my place with you a very good one."

"It can't be better than many others you have had," said she.

"In some ways it is much the best I have ever enjoyed," I responded.

"At all events, it isn't half as good as you deserve," the Angel cried warmly. "I should like to see you in one far more desirable."

"Thank you," said I meekly. "So should I, of course, though I should wish it still to be in your service."

"If that could be," she murmured, with a slight blush and a flattering air of regret. "I don't quite see how it could. But if you wouldn't mind going to America, perhaps my father might help you to something really worth while."

"Nothing could be better for me than to have his help in obtaining what I want," said I boldly, knowing she wouldn't suspect the double meaning. "You are very good I can't thank you enough."

"Wait till I have done something to be thanked for," said she. "I will write to my father. But even if anything comes of it, it can't be for some time. Meanwhile, I suppose you will be taking Mr. Winston's car back to England, when we part at Cannes."

"Part at Cannes!" The words were a knell. "You aren't thinking, then, of going further for a trip into Italy?" I ventured.

"No, I haven't thought of it," she said.

"It does seem a pity, with Italy next door, so to speak," said I. "Unless, of course, you're tired of motoring and would like to settle down and have some gaiety."

"I'm not tired of motoring," she exclaimed, "and I'm not pining for gaiety. I think this sort of free, open-air life, with big horizons round one, spoils one for dancing and dressing and flir—and all that. I should love just to have a glimpse of the Riviera, and then go on. But I hadn't thought of it, and I'm not sure if it could be managed. I'd have to reflect upon the idea a little, and cable my father to see if he were willing. Not that there'd be much trouble about that. He trusts me, and almost always lets me do what I like. But supposing—just *supposing* I changed my plans—would Mr. Winston be willing to let me keep his car longer?"

"As much longer as you choose," said I eagerly. "He doesn't want it in England till next summer. I'm certain of that."

"Well, then, I must think it over," she answered. "Oh, it would be glorious! Yet—I don't know. Anyway, we must take Lady Brighthelmston, Mr Winston's mother, a drive on her son's car when we get to Cannes. She is staying there."

"Oh, is she?" I said aloud. And inwardly I prayed that I might see the lady in question in private before that invitation was given. But perhaps she will have flitted. I wonder?

Well, I have given you the principal points of our conversation enough to show you why I am happy to-night. But if you could have seen me cutting up the Goddess's *filet mignon!* I could have shed tears of joy on it.

Now I must be off to my own hotel, and to-morrow I shall be up with the dawn in search of a mechanic and new parts for the car.

Good-bye, old man.   Wish me luck.

Yours ever,

JACK WINSTON.

MOLLY RANDOLPH TO HER FATHER

HOTEL ANGST, BORDIGHERA,
December 25.

Merry Christmas, my dear Santa Klaus, merry Christmas! This morning I sent you a long cable, expressing my sentiments. It does seem strange to think that by this time you have it. A thousand thousand thanks for your letter and the enclosure at Cannes. You are the dearest Dad!

Our first Christmas apart! and may it be the last. Christmas isn't Christmas without you and a stocking to hang up, and I'm awfully homesick. Still, if one can't be spirited away home on a magic carpet, this is the sweetest place to spend Christmas in you can imagine.

Speaking of magic carpets recalls the *Arabian Nights*, and gives me a simile. For a whole week I've been realising what Aladdin must have felt when the Genie took him into the wonderful Cave of Jewels. Oh, the Riviera! But you know it, dear. You spent your honeymoon with the beautiful little mother whom I never knew in the Riviera and in Italy. That is one reason why I want to see Italy— why I sent that question to you by cable the other day. Your one journey abroad, dear, dear old Dad! I can guess now why you have never been keen to

BORDIGHERA.

come again, though you have always pretended you preferred Wall Street to all Europe. Now I am seeing these fairylike places I know how you have wished to keep the memory unspoiled; for they would never, never be the same if you saw them for the second time, even with me, though you do love me dearly, don't you? It's *first* times that are so thrilling; and I'm having my first times now, though they're different from yours. I don't suppose I shall ever have such a love in my life as you had, or if I do, it will be sad and broken. Either the man I could care for would be divided from me by an impassable barrier, or something else horrid will happen. I feel that. I shall never write like this again, but I can't help it to-night. There! I won't go on about your past and my future any more; but just about the "winged present." And, oh, its wings are of rainbows!

Elderly people I've talked to at hotels during the last few days tell me the "Riviera is being ruined." You would say so too perhaps; but it seems heaven to me, from Hyères to Bordighera—as far as we've gone. Just here I must stop and thank you for your answer to my cable and saying "Italy by all means." If it hadn't been for that, we shouldn't be here.

I thought that we couldn't see anything more beautiful than on the other side of Marseilles; but the Riviera is a thing apart. I'm gratefully glad to have come into such an enchanted land of sunshine and flowers on an automobile instead of a stuffy train. There's nothing in the world to equal travelling on a motor-car. You can go fast or slow; you can stop where you like and as long as you like; with a little luggage on your car you're as independent as a bird; and like a bird you float through the open air, with no thought for time-tables. When will the poet come who will sing the song of the motor-car? Maeterlinck has sung it in prose, but the song was too short.

Of course, after that horrid affair the other side of Toulon I couldn't let Jimmy drive any more. He realised that I distrusted him and rather sulkily resigned the wheel, blaming the car for the accident and declaring that it could not have happened to his Panhard, which, of course, is silly. So Brown took the helm again, and Jimmy sat in the *tonneau* with Aunt Mary, where they whispered and chuckled a good deal together, appearing to have a real live mystery up their sleeves, which I suppose had something to do with the promised surprise at Cannes.

It was quite late in the day before the steering-gear was mended and we could take the road again, and then we all thought it a pity to run through the dark to Cannes, so we decided to stay a second night in Toulon, at the same hotel where I had dinner with Brown; he, poor fellow, being this time banished to some invisible lower region, or another hotel, for Aunt Mary and Jimmy would have had fits if I had proposed that he should make a fourth at our table. I thought the people of the hotel and the head waiter looked curiously at me; for one night they saw me dine with a gentleman who the next night drives to the door as my *chauffeur* (I assure you,

Dad, it's no stretch of language to speak of Brown
as a "gentleman," and you really must get him a
gentleman's berth, even if it's way off in Klondyke).

Early next morning we started for what proved
to be the most beautiful drive we have yet had, as
warm as summer, and sparkling with sunshine. We
bowled along at a gentle pace through a fairyland
of flowers and rivers, with billowy blue mountains
rising into the sky, and showing here and there a
distant ethereal peak of snow. Very soon we passed
through Hyères, which Brown called the gate of the
Riviera, and I should have liked to turn aside for
a peep at Costebelle, which Brown thinks one of the
loveliest places of all. But Aunt Mary and Jimmy
both opposed me, saying that we ought to get on
as soon as possible to Cannes—"to Cannes" was
their constant cry.

Beyond Hyères the road became more and more
superb. We were travelling now along the mountains of the Moors, gliding through groves of oak
and woods of shimmering grey-green olives, with
glimpses of the glittering sea on our right hand.
Presently the way dipped to the verge of the sea
as far as Fréjus, from which place it rose again to
wind up and up into the heart of the Esterels. Though
we mounted many hundreds of feet, the road was
so well engineered that gradients were not very
trying. Our agreeable Napier, at any rate, made
nothing of them, but simply flew up at twelve or
fourteen miles an hour. And the descent on the
other side! My heart comes into my mouth when
I think of it. "It's quite safe," said Brown; but it

looked the most breakneck thing in the world, and my very toes seemed to curl up, not with fear, but with a kind of awful joy. I think when a bird takes its great swoops through the air it must feel like we felt that day. The car bounded down the long lengths of looped road, slowed up a little at the turns (where we all had to throw our bodies sideways, like sailors hanging over the gunwale of a racing yacht), bounded forward again so that the wind rushed by our ears like a hurricane, slowed up once more, and so by a series of these magnificent bird-like swoops reached the level ground. It was a fine piece of driving on Brown's part, needing nerve, judgment, and a perfect knowledge of the capabilities of his car. I had scarcely recovered from the tingling joy of this wild mountain descent when we were in Cannes, driving up an avenue to our hotel.

It was a charming house, and I fell in love with Cannes at first sight; but would you believe it? Jimmy's wonderful surprise never came off at all!— and he wouldn't even tell me what it was. Aunt Mary wanted to; but he got quite red, and said, "No, Miss Kedison, it may make me a great deal of trouble if you say anything—at present. The whole position is changed." I think mysteries are silly.

By the way, you remember my telling you about the nice Lady Brighthelmston I met in Paris, on her way to the Riviera—the mother of the Honourable John who owns our Napier? She was going to stay at this very hotel, and I thought it would be rather nice to see her again. I meant to ask, when we arrived at the hotel, if she were there; but to my surprise Aunt Mary remembered to do it before I did, and she and Jimmy both seemed eager to find out. We had hardly got into the big, beautiful hall, when they began to ply the manager with questions, and Jimmy looked quite crestfallen when he was told that she had just gone on to Rome. He *is* rather fond of what he calls "swells," but I hadn't fancied from what he said before that he knew Lady Brighthelmston very well, or cared particularly about meeting her.

"Most annoying!" he exclaimed crossly, glaring at the manager as if it were his fault. "And has the Honourable John Winston, her son, been here also?"

"No," said the manager. "Lady Brighthelmston was with friends, an old gentleman and his daughter. But I understood that her ladyship's son was expected and that she was disappointed he did not arrive before she and her party went away. Lady Brighthelmston left a letter for Mr. Winston," and he pointed to a letter in the rack close by the office addressed in a large handwriting to the Honourable John Winston.

I was quite frightened when I heard that the owner of my car was expected to arrive in Cannes, for Brown was so certain that he was in England; yet here he might walk in at any moment to say that he'd changed his mind and wanted back his Napier. Just as I was thinking of going on to Italy in it, too! Why, the very thought that maybe I should have to lose the car made me long to keep it all the more.

I was gazing reproachfully at the letter and wondering if we hadn't better hurry away from Cannes before the H. J. turned up, when I saw Aunt Mary lay her hand on Jimmy's arm in a warning kind of way, as if she wanted to keep him from saying something he had begun to say. At that moment I found that Brown was at my elbow, though whether Aunt Mary's warning to Jimmy had anything to do with him or not I don't know. I don't see why it should, but she did look rather funny. Brown had come in to bring me my dear little gold-netted purse with my monogram in rubies and diamonds that you gave me just before I started. I'd dropped it off my lap when I got out of the car, so you see I'm as bad about that as ever. I thanked Brown, and then drawing him aside a little, I told him about Mr. Winston and what I was afraid of. He was as sure as ever that his old master wouldn't turn up to spoil sport, though I pointed out the letter; and it's a funny thing that the Hon. J.'s ex-*chauffeur* should be kept more in touch with his movements than his own mother. However, that's not my business.

That afternoon Aunt Mary, Jimmy, and I had a lovely walk in Cannes by the sea. We had tea at a fascinating confectioner's called Rumpelmayer, and a long time afterwards dined at a perfect dream of a little restaurant built out into the sea—the Restaurant de la Réserve, something like the one in Marseilles. I wonder if they were here in your day,

Dad? There are pens in the water built up with walls, and lobsters and other creatures are swimming unsuspectingly about in them. You select your own fish, and in a few minutes the poor thing, so happy a little while ago, is on the table exquisitely cooked with its own appropriate sauce. It seems sad. Still, one does give them honourable burial, and they couldn't expect to live for ever. I let Jimmy choose mine, though, and while he and Aunt Mary discussed the *langouste* I leaned on the railing looking out over the bay. You will remember that scene— all the twinkling lights of the town, and the tumbled mass of the Esterel mountains, sombre and strange, across the sea.

At dinner I began to hint to Aunt Mary about going on to Italy, but I was rather sorry I'd said anything, for Jimmy caught me up like a flash, and exclaimed that if we did make up our minds to such a trip, he would like to keep us company on his Panhard, which he should no doubt find waiting for him at Nice. Aunt Mary asked if we should be likely to meet Lord Lane, as she had heard Jimmy talk so often of his friend Montie that she quite longed to know him. She loves a lord, poor Aunt Mary, and her face fell several inches when Jimmy answered that Montie was a very retiring chap, shy with ladies, and might make a point of keeping out of the way. When we got home to the hotel I had such a start. The Honourable John's letter was gone out of the rack. I made sure that all would now be over between the Napier and me, unless I could get so far away with it that he'd sooner hire another than follow up his; and anyway, if we disappeared he wouldn't know where to find us. I suppose that was very bad and sly of me, wasn't it? I sent word to Brown that we'd start at nine o'clock next morning; and wasn't it a joke on me, after we'd been on the road for a while I told him what had happened, and it turned out that *he'd* taken the letter to re-address to his master?

Just before we started Jimmy said he'd had a wire from Lord Lane that his car was waiting for him at the *garage* in the Boulevard Gambetta at Nice, and we went there after our splendid drive from Cannes, as Brown knew about the place, and thought it would be convenient to leave our Napier there.

We sent our luggage by cab to our hotel, lunched at a delightful restaurant, and in the afternoon, said Jimmy gaily, "I'll race you to Monte and back with my Panhard." I knew in a minute what he meant, but Aunt Mary thought he was talking about his everlasting Lord Lane, and was so disappointed to find it was only Monte Carlo. *His* Montie, he explained, was seedy and confined to bed but he hoped we wouldn't mention this before Brown, as Lord Lane didn't want his friend Jack Winston to hear that he had come to the Riviera without letting him know.

So after lunch we started away from glittering, flowery blue and white and golden Nice by the most glorious coast road for Monte Carlo. But you know it well, dear Dad. I suppose there can be nothing more beautiful on earth. And Monte Carlo is beautiful; but somehow its beauty doesn't seem real and

wholesome and natural, does it? It's like a mag-
nificently handsome woman who is radiant at night,
and doesn't look suitable to morning light, because
then you see that her hair and eyelashes are dyed and
her complexion cleverly made up. If Monte Carlo
could be concentrated and condensed into the form
of a real woman, I think she would be the kind who
uses lots of scent and doesn't often take a bath.

We wandered about among the shops and saw the
most lovely things, but somehow I didn't "feel to
want" any of them, as my nurse used to say. I
couldn't help associating all the smart hats and
dresses and jewels in the windows with the terrible
hawk faces painted to look like doves, which kept
passing us in the streets or the Casino gardens, instead of thinking whether the things would be pretty
on me.

Jimmy knows "Monte" very well, and was inclined to swagger about his knowledge. There's one
thing which I am compelled to admit that he can do
—order a dinner. He took us to a restaurant, led
aside the head waiter, talked with him for a few minutes, and announcing that dinner would be ready
when we wanted it, pioneered us across to "the
rooms." I'd seen so many pictures of the Casino
that it didn't come upon me as a surprise. The first
thing that struck me was the overpowering deadness
of the air, which felt as if generations of people had
breathed all the oxygen out of it, and the ominous,
muffled silence, broken only by the sharp chink!
chink! of the croupiers' rakes as they pulled in the
money.

Jimmy insisted on staking a louis for me and another for Aunt Mary, who was enraptured when she won thirteen louis, and would have given up dinner to go on playing if she hadn't lost her winnings and more besides.

When we sat down to our table at the restaurant she was quite depressed, but everything was so bright and gay that she soon cheered up. Our tablecloth was strewn all over with roses and huge bluey-purple violets, and the dinner was *plu*perfect. There was a great coming and going of overdressed women and rather loud young men, which amused me, but I think it would soon pall. I can't imagine any feeling of rest or peace at Monte Carlo, not even in the gardens. To stop long in the place would be like always breathing perfume or eating spice.

We had finished dinner, and Jimmy was paying the bill (I couldn't help seeing that it was of enormous length), when the scraping of chairs behind us advertised that a new party had arrived at the table back of ours. A noisy, loud-talking party it was all men, by the voices, and one of those voices sounded remotely familiar. The owner of it seemed to be telling an amusing story, which had been interrupted by entering the restaurant and taking seats. "Well, she simply jumped at it like a trout at a mayfly," the man was saying, as I sat wondering where I'd heard the voice before. "I couldn't help feeling a bit of a beast to impose on Yankee innocence. But all's fair in love and motor-cars. This was the most confounded thing ever designed;

a kind of ironmonger's shop on wheels. And the girl was deuced pretty——"

The word "motor-car" brought it all back, and in a flash I crossed Europe from the restaurant in Monte Carlo to the village hotel at Cobham. I looked round and into the face of Mr. Cecil-Lanstown.

Aunt Mary looked too, for the bill was paid, and we were getting up to go. Our eyes met in the midst of his sentence; the man half rose, but dropped down again with a silly smile, and I gave him one of those elaborate glances that begin with a person's boots and work slowly up to the necktie. Just as we were sweeping past Aunt Mary said in a loud aside to me, "Did you ever *see* such a creature? And I took him for a duke." I think he heard.

In the Casino gardens we saw the moon rise out of the sea. and never shall I forget the glory of it. But just the very beauty of everything made me feel sad. So stupid of me. I really don't think I can be well lately. I must take a tonic or a nerve pill. We went back to Nice for the night, and next morning we drove to Mentone, where I decided that I would rather stay for a long time than anywhere else on the Riviera. It is just the sweetest, dearest little picture-place, with the natural, country peacefulness that others lack, and yet there's all the gaiety and life of a town. We drove to it along the upper road, which is almost startlingly magnificent I asked Brown to go slowly, so that we might sip the scenery instead of bolting it. Though the Napier could have gone romping up the steep road out of Nice to the Observatory, and on to quaint La Turbie, I chose a pace of six or seven miles an hour, often stopping at picturesque corners to drink in sapphire draughts of sea and sky. Coming this way from Nice to Mentone we skipped Monte Carlo altogether, only looking down from La Turbie on its roofs, on the glittering Casino, and the gloomy, rock-set castle of Monaco.

And, oh, by the way, Jimmy wasn't with us on that drive, nor has he joined us yet, though he threatens to (if that word isn't too ungracious) a little farther on in Italy. He stayed behind in Nice to take care of Lord Lane. Aunt Mary thinks that shows such a sweet disposition; but I'm not sure. I believe that Montie is a marquis.

We stopped near Mentone, at Cap Martin, which of course you don't know, as it's rather new. And it was lovely there, up high on a hill, among sweet-smelling pines. It was pleasant to be alone with Aunt Mary again, and I was nicer to her than I have been, I'm afraid, since Pau and Jimmy. I should have loved to stay a long while (and it would be jolly to come back for the carnival, though I don't suppose we shall), but there was such a thrill in the thought of Italy being near that I grew restless. Italy! Italy! I heard the name ringing in my ears like the "horns of elfland."

Now we are in it—Italy, I mean, not elfland, though it seems much the same to unsophisticated me for mystery and colour; and it is good to have warm-hearted Christmas for our *first* day. The one jarring note in the Italian "entrance music" was at the frontier. I think I wrote you how, when we

landed at Dieppe from England, about a hundred
years ago, I had to pay a deposit to the custom-
house for the right to take my car into France.
That money I should have got back at Mentone on
leaving the country if the late-lamented Dragon had
still been in existence, but as it vanished in smoke
and flame the money has vanished too. Brown,
however (or, rather, Brown's master), paid a similar
deposit on the Napier, and passing the French custom-house on the outskirts of Mentone, the Lightning Conductor asked my permission to stop, that
he might present Mr. Winston's papers and get the
money back to send to England.

So far, so good; but it was dusk when we left the
Cap Martin (as we'd spent the day in exploring
Mentone), and the custom-house people have detained us some time; it was dark, cloudy, and windy
when we moved on again towards Italy. A *douanier*
mounted by Brown's side (I was with Aunt Mary
in the *tonneau*) to conduct us to the last French post,
where we dropped him; and in few yards farther
we were in Italy. Maybe you remember that the
frontier is marked by a wild chasm, cleft in the high
mountains which hurl themselves down to the very
margin of the sea. Over the splendid chasm is the
Pont St. Louis, and through the very middle of the
stone bridge runs the invisible "frontier line."

I thought I saw a sentry-box on the Italian side,
but it was too dark to be sure; and one has to go
a good way up the steep mountain road before one
reaches the office of the *douane*. Here Brown pulled
up, as two slouching men in blue-grey overcoats,

with rifles slung over their backs, came forward to meet us. Our Lightning Conductor is always very courteous in dealing with foreign officials. He says it "smooths things"; and now, seeing that the men intended to stop us, he politely expressed the wish to pass, offering to pay whatever deposit was demanded. Though I have only the smallest smattering of Italian, I could understand pretty well what followed. The men refused to let us pass. Brown argued the matter; he produced a passport, which the two men inspected by the light of a lantern. They appeared impressed, but still refused us passage, saying that the office was closed for the night, that the chief had gone, and that there was no one who could make out the necessary papers. "But it is monstrous!" cried Brown. "Is this Italian hospitality? Do you suggest that the ladies should remain here on the road till morning?" The *douaniers* shrugged their shoulders. "There are plenty of good hotels in Mentone," said one. "Go back there."

"No," said Brown, "I will not go back. Where does the chief of the bureau live?" The *douaniers* refused to tell. Clearly they did not want a "wigging" for letting loose an imperious Englishman upon their chief, reposing after his dinner. By this time an interested crowd of ten or twelve persons had assembled, their shadowy forms seeming to rise out of the ground. I heard a voice in French whisper into my ear, "I am of France, and all these Italians are pigs. The *chef de douane* lives in Mortola, the first village up the road"; and before

I could look round to thank him, the friendly Frenchman was swallowed up in darkness. I called Brown
and gave him the news. He asked if we minded
being left alone while he went to fetch the chief,
saying we should be quite safe in charge of the
douaniers; and on our agreeing strode off up the
steep road, one of the guards immediately padding
silently after him. We sat and waited perhaps half
an hour on the threshold of Italy, our lamps casting
their rays into the country we were forbidden to
enter, when I heard Brown's voice and the sound
of footsteps. By some persuasion he had induced
the *chef de douane* to return with him. The office
doors were thrown open, the gas was lighted, the
necessary papers were made out, the deposit paid,
and then, at Brown's invitation, the agreeable official
mounted into the car, and we ran quickly up the hill
to his house.

It was a thrilling drive from the frontier to
Bordighera. A great wind coming salt off the sea
was moaning along the face of the mountains, completely drowning the comforting hum of our motor.
The road mounted up and up, terrific gusts striking
the car as it came out into exposed places. Far
below we heard the thunder of mighty waves dashing
on the rock. Then we began to descend a steep and
twisting road that led up presently to low ground,
not much above the sea, where the wind shrieked
down the funnel of a river-bed. Then up again
along another face of cliff under cyclopean walls of
masonry, and down a sudden shoot between houses
into the old, old town of Ventimiglia; across a river

and a plain, to be pulled up presently by a very dangerous obstacle—a huge beam of wood, unlighted, and swung across the road to guard a level crossing. Our great acetylene eye, glaring ahead, gave Brown ample warning, and we slowed down, then stopped, while a train thundered past. Very deliberately a signalman presently came to push the barrier aside, and we darted on through a long, straggling village, turned away from the sea, found a large iron gate with a lamp over it, standing hospitably open, and twisting through a fairy-like garden studded with gigantic palms, drew up in a flood of light that poured from the door of a large white hotel. To walk into the big, bright hall, to hear pleasant English voices, to see nice men and pretty girls dressed for dinner and waiting for the stroke of the gong, was an extraordinary contrast to the roaring blackness of the night outside. Everyone turned to stare at us as we came in masked and goggled like divers.

This morning I waked up and looked out of my window a little before seven. It was just sunrise and the wind had died. Under my eyes lay the garden, lovely as Eden, garlands of roses looped from orange trees to palms; banks of heliotrope, and sweetness unutterable. Then, a waving sea of palms, with here and there the glow of a scarlet roof, and beyond the sea. The rising sun shone on it and on the curved line of coast, with Monte Carlo and Mentone gleaming like pearl. Floating up on the horizon I saw a shadowy blue shape of an island, hovering like a ghost, and as I looked it vanished suddenly as a broken bubble, leaving the sea blank.

I thought it must have been a mirage; but by-and-by a soft-speaking, fawn-eyed maid called Apollonia told me it was Corsica, which only shows itself sometimes early in the morning when the sun is at a certain height and usually after a storm.

We breakfasted in our sitting-room, with delicious honey for our crisp rolls, and afterwards, when I went downstairs to send your cable, I found the hall smelling like a forest of balsam firs. It was decorated for Christmas, and the whole hotel seemed full of a sort of joyous, Christmas stir, so that it was more like a jolly, big country-house than a hotel.

Then I found out that this hotel is famous for its Christmas celebration. Everyone stopping there was supposed to be the landlord's guest at a wonderful dinner, a regular feast, with dozens of courses, ending up with crackers, which we all pulled. Last of all the dining-room was darkened, and a long procession of waiters glided in bearing illuminated ices—green, crimson, gold, and rose. We clapped our hands and laughed, just like children, and the landlord had to make a little speech. Altogether everything was so friendly and Christmasy that the most gloomy misanthrope could not have felt homesick. I supposed when dinner was over that the special festivities were at an end. But no, quite the contrary. Everyone trooped into a huge picture-panelled recreation-room, which had been the scene of secret preparation all day, and there was a giant Christmas-tree, sparkling with pretty decorations, and heavy with presents for each person in the hotel, all provided by the landlord. We drew them with numbers, and I got a charming inlaid box with a secret opening; Aunt Mary had a little silver vase. There was music, too; harps and violins. I *was* sorry that poor Brown was cut off from all the fun. But I did give him a present. You know he refuses tips, so I couldn't offer him money; but the other day at Cannes he was looking rather worried, and it turned out that something—I didn't understand exactly what, for he was rather vague in his answers —had happened to his watch. I didn't say much then, but in Monte Carlo I bought him quite a decent one for fifty dollars (he really does deserve it), and gave it to him this morning with a "merry Christmas." You've no idea how pleased he was. He seemed quite touched.

There! a bell somewhere is striking midnight. Good-bye, dearest. My thoughts have been full of you all day.

Your

MOLLY.

JIMMY PAYNE TO CHAUNCEY RANDOLPH

GRAND HOTEL, ROME, *December 27.*

Dear Mr. Randolph,

I find myself in a difficult position, but I am going to take the bull by the horns and write to you of certain things which seem to me of importance. I trust to your friendship and your knowledge of my feelings and desires towards Molly to excuse me if you consider that I am being officious. You will understand when I have explained that I cannot hope to make her see the matter in its true light; but you, as a man and her father, will do so, and will comprehend that my motive is for her protection.

I have thanked you already for answering my letter, in which I begged that you would let me know in which part of Europe Molly was travelling, and she has told me that she wrote you of our meeting at Pau. I reached there a couple of days sooner than she and Miss Kedison did. In fact, I saw their arrival in the famous automobile of whose adventures you must have heard much. The minute my eyes lighted upon the *chauffeur* I felt an instinctive distrust of the man, and I have learned through experience not to disregard the warnings

263

of my instinct. It has served me more than one good turn in the street when the markets were wobbling. Now I have been a good deal chaffed about a resemblance to Sherlock Holmes, the great detective of fiction, but I acknowledge and am proud of that resemblance. I venture to think that it is not wholly confined to externals. A certain detective instinct was born in me. It began to show itself when I was a little boy at school, and since then I have trained and cultivated it, as a kind of higher education of the brain. In several instances I have been able to expose frauds, which, but for the purely impersonal, scientific interest I took in the affairs, might have remained undetected. In these experiments I have made enemies of course; but what matter?

The interest I feel in the case I am about to lay bare to you is not, I confess, purely impersonal. But I hope under the circumstances you will think none the less of me for that.

My first distant glimpse of the man Brown created, as I have said, an unfavourable impression upon my mind. I thought that he had a swaggering air of conceit and self-importance extremely unbecoming in a man of his class. He had the air of thinking himself equal to his betters, which is a dangerous thing in a person entrusted with the care of ladies. My impression was confirmed by some of the tales which Molly told me of her automobile experiences, not only quite unconscious that they militated against her *chauffeur*, but apparently believing them to his credit. I began to fear that the fellow was one

MENTONE FROM CAP MARTIN.

to take advantage of the trust placed in him by two unprotected women, whom he doubtless has guessed to be well provided with money. My definite suspicions went at first no further than this, though there was a kind of detective premonition in my mind that more might remain to be found out. I might have confined myself to tacit disapproval, however, or a word of advice to Molly, and perhaps one stern warning to the man, had I not gone into the golf club at Pau on our last day there. To my intense astonishment I saw Brown on the links attempting to get members to play with him by passing himself off as a gentleman. He wore good clothes, and acted his part fairly well—well enough, perhaps to deceive the unobservant. But he is not the sort of person I should ever mistake for a gentleman. I went up to him, and very quietly ordered him off the links, threatening to expose him publicly. But he whined for mercy, and I, in a moment of weak good nature, let him off, on his promise to go at once. I inquired, however, of the steward what name he had given on seeking admittance, and was startled to find that he had passed himself off as the Honourable John Winston, his late master and the owner of the car which Molly is now using. As I had bound myself to keep silence, I did not betray him, but the fact just discovered confirmed my distrust of the man as a dangerous and unscrupulous person.

For Molly's sake I felt that I must begin investigation. so as to be able in the end to expose Brown and let her see him in his real character;

but for several reasons not necessary to trouble you with it was essential to proceed with extreme caution.

It was unbearable to me, knowing even the little I did know at that time of the man's character to allow Molly and Miss Kedison to go wandering over the country alone with him. I feared that he might compromise them in some way, or even resort to blackmail, and with this danger before my mind, I offered to accompany the ladies on their car to the Riviera. I made the suggestion to Miss Kedison, not to Molly, and hinted to her something concerning my motives, cautioning her at the same time that silence was vitally important until I could give her leave to speak. You may think that I was taking a good deal on myself; but I have a great regard for you, as well as an unfortunately deep affection for Molly, and as I have made many intimate friends among the highest in the land, all over the Continent, as in England, I felt that my presence in the car might be especially helpful.

During the first day or two of our journey I caught Brown in several audacious lies. He was insolent to me, evidently afraid that I meant to lose him his berth, and inclined to be so familiar with the ladies, Molly particularly, that my suspicions of him were roused to fever heat. I began to see that his ambitions tended higher than I had at first supposed, and—I hope you will forgive my frankness—I should not be surprised if some day before long Molly should have a startling awakening.

I questioned her carefully as to what Brown had

said to her of his late master's movements, and it appeared that, according to the *chauffeur*, the Honourable John Winston had returned to England, leaving Brown to hire out and drive his automobile. This seemed strange to me, and I asked myself if it were possible that the fellow could have contrived to steal the car, and be using it for his own purposes, taking the money derived from its hire for himself. One thing which encouraged this deduction was the extremely low rent asked for the vehicle and the small wages demanded by Brown. But it was at Toulon that a still more sinister idea was forced into my mind by a startling incident to which I will draw your attention.

You will very likely have heard from Molly that owing to a side-slip which might have happened to anyone in driving an automobile, we had an upset by the roadside, and in common politeness I was compelled to obey Miss Kedison's request to remain with her at a small village, some miles from Toulon, while Molly went on to see a doctor about an injury to her wrist, Brown being her attendant. When Miss Kedison and I arrived at Toulon on the car next day, it was decided to stay the night there rather than go on so late. I saw Brown, who was working outside the hotel at the automobile, take money out of his pocket to pay a man who had been helping him with the repairs. Something small dropped on the ground as he did so, unknown to Brown. When he had moved away, I stooped and picked it up. It was a French pawn-ticket for a pledged watch, dated the previous night. I deter-

mined, in the interest of my investigations, to visit
the pawnbroker's, which I did; and giving up the
ticket, said I had called to redeem the pledge.
Imagine my sensations when I saw a magnificent gold
repeater, with the monogram "J. W." upon it in
small diamonds. The conclusion was obvious, for
the watch was not one which would be given by
a master even to the most valued servant. I paid
something like two hundred and sixty francs to
redeem the repeater, and justified such a proceeding
to myself by the argument that the watch had
assuredly been stolen, and that my action was the
most certain way of preserving it for the owner and
earning that owner's gratitude, *if he still existed*.
Those last four words, which I have underscored,
will enlighten you as to the doubts now materialising
in my mind. In fact, I believe this *chauffeur* a man
capable of anything.

On returning to the hotel, with the Honourable
Mr. Winston's watch in my pocket, I made a few
inquiries as to Brown's behaviour the night before;
I learned that he had appeared in the *salle à manger*
for dinner, in an irreproachable evening suit which
in some way he must have obtained from his master.
Perhaps I ought not to repeat what else I learned, as
I do not like to tell tales out of school, but I think
it is only right you should know that Molly allowed
this impostor to sit at the table with her, as if he had
been an equal instead of a servant.

I positively dared not let Miss Kedison into the
secret of what had happened, but I hinted to her
that I had had good reason to think less well of

Brown even than before. It was arranged that we should induce Molly to hurry on to Cannes, where Lady Brighthelmston (pronounced "Brighton"), the mother of my friend the Honourable John Winston, was supposed to be staying. I wished to find out from her when she had last heard from her son, and if she were absolutely assured of his present safety. I also intended to show her the watch, and put her in possession of all the deductions and details I had been able to pick up. This once done, Brown's exposure by Lady Brighthelmston and subsequent dismissal by Molly would be only a question of hours.

Unfortunately, however, Lady Brighthelmston had left Cannes for Rome when we arrived; nevertheless, one more proof of the *chauffeur's* duplicity came into my hands there. A letter which had been left in the rack for the Honourable John Winston, by his mother, was secretly *taken out by Brown*. And the fact that Lady Brighthelmston was expecting her son to join her on his automobile does not look as if poor Jack were in England and had voluntarily left his car with the *chauffeur*.

Altogether the affair appears ominous for my friend, and the thought that Molly and Miss Kedison are perpetually at the mercy of this unscrupulous wretch, in a strange country, is maddening to me as it will be to you when you receive this letter. When they left the Riviera for Italy, I was obliged to remain behind for a day with a sick friend, but followed as soon as possible on my Panhard. Owing, however, to unforeseen events and one or two small accidents, I was delayed, and unable to catch them up as I had intended. Finally, as Brown was probably hurrying on with the express intention of making it impossible for me to overtake the party, I determined to abandon my car and proceed by rail to Rome, their destination. My idea was to reach that city before they could do so, and see Lady Brighthelmston as I had planned to do at Cannes, so that the police could be ready if necessary to arrest Brown immediately on his arrival. I arrived on the day expected and called at the hotel to which Lady Brighthelmston's letters were to be forwarded from Cannes. But on account of the unusual cold and bad weather, she had suffered from neuralgia, and had gone on with her friends, after less than a week's stay, to Naples, with the idea that she might visit Sicily later.

Having gone so far, I am not to be turned back. I love Molly far too well to desert her, and some day, when she finds out all I have done for her sake, perhaps she will appreciate me better than she has up to the present. I cannot tell her myself, but it may be that you will think fit to let her know. I mean to follow Lady Brighthelmston to Naples, or even farther if it be necessary, for writing the information I have to give might do more harm than good to everyone concerned. I must be on the spot; but very unluckily I cannot be there for some days to come. The weather in Rome is really awful, and I have contracted something which I am afraid is influenza. With the best intentions, I cannot go to the rescue until the doctor gives me leave. I shall

probably still be here when Molly arrives. Meanwhile, my dear Mr. Randolph, I have thought best to
put you on your guard.

Yours faithfully and sincerely,

J. F. PAYNE.

MOLLY RANDOLPH TO HER FATHER

Hotel de Russie, Rome,
January 2.

Darling Dad,

Forgive me for that inadequate little note written yesterday to wish you a Happy New Year; but short as it was, there was enough love in it to make the letter double postage. We have been working so hard at pleasure since that I haven't had time for anything except the various cables which from day to day I have flung to you from our chariot of fire as we sped half-way down the long leg of Italy —that's pink on my schoolroom map at home. Somehow, I've always thought of Italy as being pink, ever since I first hunted it out on the map; and it is still gloriously *couleur de rose* to the eyes of my body and mind.

How splendid it is not to be disappointed in something that you've looked forward to all your life, isn't it? But I don't think I am the kind of girl who is disappointed in *real* things—nature's real things, I mean. People have often said to me, "Oh, you will be disappointed in Europe, if you look forward to it so much." But I believe such creatures have no imagination. With imagination you have the glamour of the past and all the wonderful things that have happened in a place, as well as the mere beauty of the present. But then, without imagination one must just expect to have one's poor little soul go bare, and to live on all the "cold pieces" of life, never to taste the nectar and ambrosia of the gods; never to know the thrill of sympathy, or any other thrill that isn't purely physical.

I'm intoxicated with all I have seen and am seeing —which must excuse the harangue. And I'm intoxicated with the joy of driving the car. Lately I have been rivalling the Lightning Conductor, for my wrist is quite well again. The microbe of automobilism has entered into my blood. Yes, I'm speaking literally; I'm sure there's such a microbe, and that he's a brave beast. I should like to see him in your big microscope. Perhaps I'll bring him home for the purpose.

It has become the greatest joy I have ever known to get all I possibly can out of noble Balzac; to urge Balzac uphill as fast as I can; to drive Balzac downhill as fast as I dare; to manœuvre Balzac in and out of traffic with all my skill and nerve. But you mustn't be a bit uneasy about me. Brown is always at my elbow to "warn, to comfort, to command," and I know that he won't let me do anything I oughtn't or let any harm come of it if I did.

The worst of driving an automobile yourself, when you've really got that microbe in your blood, is that you don't see quite as much of the country as you would otherwise, and that you hate to stop, even when there are wonderful things to see. But then it used to be almost the same in both ways when one lived, breathed, and moved for bicycles. Do you remember how I would talk of nothing else, and made "bike slang" answer for all human nature's daily needs? You *were* annoyed one night when I took your arm as we were walking together, and told you you were "geared too high for me."

If my life depended now on giving accurate details of the country through which we've been driving, I should have to resign myself to die. I only know that I've never been so happy, or seen half so much that was beautiful and (as that Mrs. Bennett, who wanted to marry you so badly, was always saying) "soul-satisfying."

Well, we left Bordighera the day after Christmas. Brown called it "Boxing Day," but I didn't understand what he meant till he explained. We went spinning along the Riviera di Ponente, towards Genoa la Superba, where we were to halt for the night. Perhaps—just perhaps—a true critic of beauty, whose blood had cooled with much experience, would say that the Italian Riviera road wasn't quite equal to the French between Cannes and Mentone. But it's Italy, Italy! And there's the difference of charm between the two (as I said to Brown) that there is between a magnificent young French Duchesse, confident of her own charms, with generations of breeding and wealth behind her, and a lovely, peach-tinted, simple-hearted Italian peasant girl. How rich the colour is everywhere!—and yet it never seems to dazzle the eye. I suppose it's the wonderful atmosphere that harmonises everything. And then the lovely, softening effect of the years; the moss, the lichen; the endearing dilapidation! So many things appeal to your *heart* as you pass through Italy. Oh I don't know how to describe it; but luckily you've been here, and we generally feel things alike, you and I; so you'll know what I mean. Poor little pathetic houses, painted red, blue, or yellow! You laugh at them, and want to cry over them, and love them, too. And the reds, yellows, and blues are like no other reds, yellows, and blues in the world. Fancy, if we had houses like that in our new land! How frightful they would be! We would want the painters to be put in prison for their crime.

I can tell you this: That first day of ours was like hurrying through a whole gallery of Turner's paintings. I love Turner, and I often wonder if *my* world isn't as different from many people's old grey worlds as his was!

Another thing, we had become phenomenal. That is, we were in a motor-car-less region. Ours was the only car, whereas on the other side of Mentone we met a rival every ten minutes. I do get cause and effect so mixed up. Aren't there many automobiles in Italy because there are such lots of places where you can't buy petrol; or can't you buy petrol because people won't go in automobiles?

We went flashing along past pretty little Ospedaletti, with its big white casino, and into gay and colourful San Remo, where we bought inferior petrol and paid twice as much for it as in France. I wonder if any small watering-place ever had as many attractive-looking hotels in it as San Remo? If I

were staying there, I should weep because I couldn't
live in them all at once.   But one would be obliged
to have about thirty astral bodies to go round, and
each one would have to be a well-dressed astral body.
That would come expensive; or do astral bodies
exude frocks, so to speak?

I insisted on stopping for a few moments within
sight of Taggia, because a great friend of mine lived
there, or rather, the author of his being.   His name
was "Doctor Antonio," and he existed in the pages
of a book written by a famous Italian, John Ruffini.
Brown gave me the book for a Christmas present,
apologising for the liberty; but, you see, it was all
about Bordighera, and he thought I would like to
have it.   So I did, for it is one of the most enchant-
ing stories I have ever read, though written in an
old-fashioned style, and also with a pretty little
heroine who was so old-fashionedly meek I could
have shaken her.   I sat up nearly all night reading
the book, and oh, how I cried!   There never was
such a splendid fellow in real life as Doctor Antonio,
except, of course, you.   And, do you know, if Brown
had been born a gentleman I think *he* might have
turned out something like that.   I liked Taggia for
Doctor Antonio's sake; and I admired Porto Maurizio on its haughty promontory.   It towers in my
recollection just as the real Porto Maurizio towers
above the indigo-blue sea, out of which it seems to
grow.

If it hadn't been for Brown, I'm ashamed to say
I shouldn't have known much about the Ligurian
Alps.   Do you, Dad?   They're frightfully interest-

ing, a sort of "bed rock" of Italian history. Dear me,
how ignorant one can be, when all the while one is
quite pleased with oneself as an Educated Person,
with a capital E and P.

Alassio I thought a dear little place. You stopped
there when you were coaching, in your honeymoon
days. How little you dreamed then that your
daughter would go tearing through on a motor? It
has a nicer beach than any of the rival towns we
saw; no wonder the Italians love to bathe there!
Brown told me interesting stories about the enormous, lofty brick towers of Albenza, that seemed to
nod so drowsily over the narrow, shadowed streets;
Savona was too much modernised to please me,
though the name had chimed alluringly in my ears;
and with Prà we were treading on the trailing skirts
of Genoa. Jimmy Payne had told Aunt Mary that
it was nicer to stay all night in Pegli than in Genoa,
because there were large gardens and a splendid
view; but Brown said, if we would trust him, he
would take us to a hotel in the midst of Genoa, with
a large garden and a splendid view. So we did trust
him—at least I did. And oh, Dad, I had my first
experience in driving through real, enormous city
traffic in Genoa! I *would* try it; and I succeeded
beyond my dreams. I have got things to a fine
point now, so that I manipulate the clutch and
throttle (don't they sound murderous?) almost auto-
matically; and there's something quite magical in
the ease with which one can bring the car instantly
down to a crawling walk, which wouldn't disconcert
a tortoise, behind a string of carts, or at a touch dart

ahead of the string, and leave the swiftest horse as if he were standing still.

There must be comparatively few automobiles in Genoa, or else ours beat the record for beauty; for people in the long, straight, narrow old streets lined with palaces, or the wide, stately, newer streets of splendid shops (where they showed everything on earth except the Genoa velvet I had always yearned to see on its native heath) turned to stare at us. But oh, perhaps it was only because a girl was driving! Anyway, the girl didn't disgrace herself. You would have been proud to see her daringly steer down an old sloping causeway into the Garden of Eden—I mean, the garden of our hotel. Anyway, the girl was proud of herself when the Lightning Conductor said, "Brava! No one could have done that better."

Brown was quite right about coming on to Genoa. It was a lovely hotel, with quite a tropical garden that had a sort of private Zoo of its own; jolly little beasts and birds in cages, which Aunt Mary and I fed next morning, when we'd had a delicious rest after a long day. After an early breakfast we went sight-seeing; and isn't the Campo Santo the very quaintest thing you ever saw? I don't think I could have helped laughing at some of the extraordinary marble ladies (with hoop skirts and bustles, and embroidered granite ruffles, and stone roses in their bonnets, kissing the hands of angel husbands with mutton-chop whiskers and elastic-sided boots; or knocking at the doors of forbidding-looking tombs, with Death as a sort of unliveried footman saying,

"Not at home") if it hadn't been for the mourners coming to visit their dead. Oh, the pathos of them, with their sad, dark eyes, their heavy black draperies, and the flowers they were bringing to tell their loved ones that they were never forgotten! Instead of laughing, I came near crying. But the two moods are often so near together that one makes mistakes in their identity. The only fine and simple thing in the huge, strange place was the tomb of Mazzini.

I was tremendously impressed with the harbour at Genoa. It seemed so proud, as if Italy need have no shame to be represented by it, in the presence of all the crowding ships from all the ports of the world.

The morning was still young and fair when we rushed away along the Riviera di Levante; and even Aunt Mary was congratulating herself that we were on an automobile and not a train. For a while our road ran side by side with the rail; and whenever the coast was at its most exquisite, with some jutting headland over which we could skim like a bird, the wretched train had to go burrowing through the earth like a mole, all the glory and beauty shut out in murky darkness. I counted about fifty tunnels between Genoa and Spezzia. When we'd escaped from the suburbs of Genoa, and the last tall houses which made you afraid it might be their day to fall, we came upon visions as lovely as any we had seen in the French Riviera. Those gleaming towns set on curving bays of sapphire will always seem like dream-towns to me, unless I go back and prove their reality; especially Rapallo, which was the most beautiful of all. Jennie Harborough and her mother

spent all one winter there, I remember their telling
me, and were sorry to go at the end. They went
because it was rather cheap, but stayed because it
was more lovely than the expensive places. From
Rapallo, through Zoagli to Chiavari, we were high
above the sea, winding through ravine after ravine,
but at Chiavari the best of the coast was behind us;
and at Sestri, much to our disgust, we had to turn
our backs on the sea. Still, it was delicious mounting up among the foothills of the Apennines by the
Col di Baracca, and running down to Spezzia, lying
like a pretty, lazy woman, looking out upon the green
gulf named after it. We had lunch in a cool, agreeable hotel to which I felt grateful because of its pretty
name—the Croce di Malta. I did want to go and
see Shelley's house at Lerici, but—well, I saw its
photograph instead; for there was our Napier "sleeping with one valve open," luring us on, on under the
shadow of the Apennines. One *does* feel a wretch
always "going on" instead of lingering, but that
microbe I told you about gives one a fever. Think
of running through Lucca! But, if we did what we
planned in the day we must sacrifice something, so we
sacrificed Lucca to Pisa. The very name, before our
arrival, made me a child again, looking through the
big stereoscope in your study at the Leaning Tower,
or at the steel engraving in Finden's *Landscape
Annual*. But from the moment I saw it, like a
carving in ivory, reclining gracefully on the bosom
of a golden cloud, I forgot the stereoscope and the
Annual. In future I shall always see it against that
cloud of rosy sunset-gold.

I never knew how beautiful marble could be until I came to Pisa and *Rome*. Somehow I had associated Pisa with the Leaning Tower, and not with the Baptistry. I knew it existed, and, vaguely, that it was worth seeing; but Pisa meant the Leaning Tower to me. Now I couldn't tell you which has left the deeper impression. I'm not at all the same girl that I was before I put Pisa and Rome into the gallery of my mind. I *must* make myself a worthy frame for such pictures as I am storing up now. I have the feeling not only that I want to read better books, hear more splendid music, and do more noble things, but that I shall know how to appreciate more clearly everything that is exalted or exalting. I hope you won't think me sentimental to say that.

We stayed all night at a real Italian hotel on the Lung Arno. Brown suggested it, thinking that we might enjoy an experience thoroughly characteristic of the country through which we were flying so fast. Aunt Mary wasn't pleased with the idea at all, said it would be horrid, and prophesied unspeakable things; but, as usual, Brown proved to be right, and she consented to admit it if I would promise not to punish her with her own stock phrase—"I told you so!" You would have laughed to see me conscientiously trying to eat maccaroni in the true Italian way. I curled it round my fork beautifully, but the hateful thing *would* uncurl again before I could get it up to my mouth, and accidents happened.

I watched the Italians, too, pouring their wine from the fat glass flasks swung in pivoted cradles. They did it all with one hand, holding a goblet between the thumb and second finger, and twisting the index finger round the neck of the bottle to pull it forward. It looked such a neat and simple trick that I thought I could do likewise; but—well, it was the reverse of neat when I did it, and the spotless tablecloth was spotless no longer. Instead of glaring at me for the mischief I had done, the head waiter was all sympathy. How nice and Italian of him!

That night, lying between sheets that smelt of lavender—only better than American or English lavender—I lived through the day once more, seeing ruined watch-towers set on hills, old grey monasteries falling into beautiful decay, or apparitions of white marble cathedrals. Then, over and over again, that wonderful carved-ivory tower leaning against the golden sky came back to me—so *clean*, so uninjured by the reverent centuries, and the sound of the angel-voiced echo in the Baptistry, and the strange shapes of the dear beasts supporting the pulpit, just like I used to picture the beasts in Revelations when I was a little girl. Next morning I had another look at the Leaning Tower before we started, and in a shop I came across a delicious and beautifully written book called *In Tuscany*, by the English Consul at Leghorn, so I bought it, and now I know as much as Brown does about the country through which we passed during several perfect days.

I'm not sure, but I am being both brutal and banal in saying that the rest of our journey to Rome was comparatively uninteresting. Of course, nothing can be *really* uninteresting in Italy, but I suppose those first days had spoiled me. We drove for mile after

mile through marshy land, where tall, melancholy
eucalyptus trees told their tale of a brave struggle
against malaria. All the windows and doors of the
signal cabins by the railway stations were protected
by wire gauze against mosquitoes, and we who have
spent summers on Staten Island know what *that*
means, don't we?

I think, if I were not in Rome, I could have
written you a better account of our flight through
Italy; but the Eternal City has blurred all other
impressions for me now, though I think afterwards
they will come back as clear and bright as ever.
Nevertheless, I'm not going to write you much about
Rome. It's too big for my pen, too mighty and too
marvellous. I can only feel. You have been here,
and Rome doesn't change. Only I *wonder* what you
felt when you first saw the Laocoön and the Apollo
Belvedere? I used to think I didn't quite appreciate
sculpture, but now I know it was because something
in me was waiting for the *best*, and refusing to be
satisfied with what was less than the best. Why, I
didn't even know what *marble* could be till I saw the
Laocoön. I had meant to do a good deal of sight-
seeing that day when I began with the Vatican; but
I sat for hours in front of those writhing figures in
their eternal torture. I couldn't go away. The
statue seemed to belong to me, and I had found it
again, after searching hundreds and hundreds of
years. I wonder if I was once a princess in the
palace of the Cæsars, in another state of existence,
and if in those days I used to stand and worship the
Laocoön? I shouldn't wonder a bit. And the Apollo

Belvedere! What a gentleman—what a *perfect gentleman* he is! You will laugh at me for such a thought. It seems commonplace, but it isn't. Nobody's ever said it before. He's such a gentleman and so graciously beautiful that you know he must be a god. I shouldn't have minded worshipping him a bit. Paganism had its points.

I should love to come back to Rome on my wedding trip if I were married to exactly the right man; but if he were not *exactly* right I should kill him; whereas in ordinary places I might be able to stand him well enough, as well as most women stand their husbands. Speaking of men who aren't exactly right reminds me of Jimmy Payne. He is here. He seems to have a sort of instinct to tell him when one is about to drive up to a hotel, and then he stations himself in the door, expecting the blessing which is for those who stand and wait. We made a sensation driving down the narrow Corso at the fashionable hour, and Jimmy got some of the credit of it when he stepped forward to welcome us. He had heard me say that we would stop here, because I'd been told it was the only hotel in Rome with a garden, and was close to the Pincian; and Jimmy has such a way of remembering things you say, if he thinks it's to his advantage. His first appearance was slightly marred, however, by a sneeze which, like Lady Macbeth's etcetera spot, would "out" at the precise moment of shaking hands. He says he got influenza from the Duchessa di Something-or-Other, upon whom he was obliged to call the instant he arrived, or she would never have forgiven him; so of course it's not quite so hard to bear as common, second-class influenza. It appears that he was so anxious to see "dear Lady Brighthelmston before she could get away" that he shed his automobile at Genoa, and hurried on by train, though whether on receipt of a telegraphic bidding from her ladyship or not I don't know. Anyway, she didn't wait for him, or else the influenza frightened her; for she has gone, and apparently without leaving word for poor disconsolate Jimmy. She was at his hotel, and left word with the manager that she would wire when she was settled in "some place where there was a *little* sunshine" for her letters to be forwarded. He is waiting till that wire arrives.

Jimmy is "thick as thieves" with Aunt Mary, but as frigid as a whole iceberg to poor Brown, if they happen to run across each other. I do think, don't you, Dad, that it shows shocking bad breeding to be nasty to a person who, from the very nature of the case, can't answer back? When I hear people speaking rudely to servants I always set them down as cads. Imagine marrying a man and then finding out that he was a cad! One ought to be able to get a divorce. The weather has, I suppose, been terrible since we came to Rome; at least, I hear everyone in our hotel grumbling, and certainly gardens haven't been of much use to us. But I am in a mood not to mind weather. I am in Rome. I say that over to myself, and I read *Lanciani* and *Hare*, and then I don't know whether it rains or not. Besides, yesterday was clear on purpose for me to walk in the Pincian and Borghese Gardens. Brown had to go with me because Aunt Mary was afraid there would be another storm; and besides, some little English ladies she has met in our hotel had invited her to have tea with them in their bedroom. They make it themselves with their own things, because then you don't have to pay; and if there aren't enough cups to go round among the ladies they've asked, they take their tooth-brush glasses for themselves. And they bring in custardy cakes in paper-bags and cream in tiny pails which they hide in their muffs, and try to look unconscious. There are a lot here like that, and they stay all winter. None of them are married, and they all do and say exactly the things you know they will beforehand. Why, just to look at them you feel sure they'd have tatting on their stays, and make their own garters. But some of them are titled, or if they're not they talk a great deal about being "well connected"; and they do nothing on weekdays but read novels, work in worsteds, and play bridge with the windows hermetically sealed; or on Sundays but go to the English church. Only think, and they're in *Rome!*

I haven't wasted one minute since we came, but, thank goodness, I'm not trying to "*do*" Rome scientifically and exhaustively like so many poor wilted-looking Americans I've met here. They think they must see every picture in every gallery, and put at least their noses inside every church; and then they scribble things down in their note-books—things which will do them just as much good afterwards as Lizard Bill's writings on his slate when the ink trickled over his nose, in *Alice's Adventures*. One

American lady in this hotel said her daughters had dragged her about so much that she didn't know what country she was in any more, except by the postage stamps. If I were in her place I should lie down to take a nap when I arrived in town, and *say* I had seen the things when I went back to Fond du Lac; there's where she lived before her daughters took to doing Paris in one day and London in two; they told me quite simply that was the time you needed to give.

Dad, *we drove in the automobile along the Appian Way*. It sounds shocking, but it wasn't; it was glorious. There is never anything jarring (I don't mean that for a pun) about going into the midst of old and wonderful things on a motor-car, for *it* is wonderful too, and it has a dignity of its own—the dignity of fine and perfect mechanism which seems alive, like a splendid Pegasus or an obedient unicorn, or some other strange legendary animal which you are obliged to respect and marvel at.

And Brown took me into the Colosseum last night —late—when the moon was rising out of torn black clouds.

But I said I wasn't going to write about Rome, and I won't—I vow I won't, not even about St. Peter's. I think one ought to stop here ten days, and see things all day long—just things you want to see, not things you ought to see; or else linger for months, and let everything soak into your soul. I can't do the latter, this time, with the Napier waiting —waiting; and so I'm making the best of the first.

Your reincarnated Roman Princess,

MOLLY.

FROM MOLLY RANDOLPH TO HER FATHER

PARKER'S HOTEL, NAPLES,
January 13.

You Dear,

I have seen Naples, but I don't wish to die. Not that I should so much grudge dying after the happy life you've given me, but there'd be such an awful waste of time in staying dead when so much is left to see. There's Capri, and there's Sicily almost next door; and even a Saturday to Monday on Mars wouldn't make up to me for missing them.

We put our hands to the plough, and came here from Rome in six hours, only one hour more than the fast (?) train takes. We didn't stop for lunch, but kept ourselves up on beef lozenges, which were nasty but supporting. We wanted to see how quickly we *could* do it, and even Aunt Mary was excited. She is much pleasanter without Jimmy, and we really did have fun. It's an ill rain that doesn't temper the dust to an automobile, so we blessed the weather which we had previously anathematised. After a pouring night, it cleared before we started; and it was one of the best days we have ever had. I remembered heaps of things which had happened to me when I was a Roman princess, two thousand years ago, and felt just as if I were travelling in my chariot from my father's palace in Rome to his villa, perhaps in Baiæ. My only fear was that, in going so fast, we should arrive at our destination so long before the impedimenta that I should have to do without my baths of asses' milk for several days; and where would be my royal complexion?

It was six o'clock, and dark, when we came in sight of something which made me cry out "Oh!" It was a dull red light, high up in the sky, and a dark shape, like a great wounded bull, with two streams of fiery blood pouring down its gored sides. Vesuvius! Brown had planned that we should see it for the first time after dark. I had wondered why he suggested not leaving Rome till twelve o'clock, when usually he is so keen on early starts, and he was evasive when I asked why. But when I had breathed that "Oh!" and had a moment to recover myself, he told me.

Dad, dear, Brown is splendid. He has *revealed* Naples to me. I can't express it in any other way, for nobody else who has told me about coming to Naples has ever done the things that we have; and they would not have occurred to Aunt Mary or me. We should have gone the ordinary round if it hadn't been for him, and when we said good-bye to her Naples would have been only a mere acquaintance of ours, not a dear and intimate friend who has told us her best secrets. In the first place, we shouldn't have known any better than to stop in some big, *obvious* sort of hotel in the noisy wasps' nest of the city, instead of coming here where the air is pure

and some of the most beautiful things in the world
in sight without turning our heads. It's such a
homelike hotel, and instead of sending to *England*
for orange marmalade made of Sicilian oranges, the
way all the other hotels seem to do, they make it
themselves out of their own oranges; and it's a poem.

We've been up Vesuvius, not in the daytime, like
the humdrum tourists, but by torchlight, and we saw
the moon rise. Instead of rushing to the Museum
the first thing and mooning vaguely about there for
hours, we saved it until after we'd been out to
Pompeii on the motor-car; then it was a hundred
times more interesting, and we are coming back
after Capri to pay another visit to the busts of
Tiberius and his terrible mother. I felt in Rome
as if it were an impertinence to be modern and
young. But in Pompeii—oh, I can't tell you what
I felt there. I think—I really do think that I saw
ghosts, and they were much more real and important
than I. It was like entering the enchanted palace of
the Sleeping Beauty in the wood, only a thousand
times more thrilling and wonderful. I didn't feel as
if anyone else had ever been there since it was dug up,
except Brown and me—and, of course, Aunt Mary.

Brown knew about fascinating Italian restaurants,
and he drove us up on the automobile for tea to a
new hotel on a high hill, almost a mountain. It's
the "smart" thing for people who know to go up to
tea, which—if it's fine—you have on a great terrace
that is the most beautiful thing in all Naples. And
we spent a whole morning up at St. Elmo. That is
going to be my best recollection, I think, and—you

will laugh—but the next best will be the Aquarium. When you came to Naples was there a thing in the Aquarium like the ghost of a cucumber, transparent as glass, with strings of opals and rubies being drawn through its veins every two minutes regularly? Brown says that it—or its ancestor—has been there ever since he can remember. I like that green light in the Aquarium, which makes you feel as if you were a mermaid under the sea, and inclined to swim instead of walk.

When we were driving up to the hotel, Brown said it was almost as steep and winding as the road from Capri to Anacapri. That speech, and gazing from our balcony at Parker's over the blue bay to the island which looks like the Sphinx rising out of the sea, have made me distracted to take the automobile to Capri. Brown "doesn't advise it," and thinks "we may have great trouble in landing," but that makes me want the adventure all the more; so we're going to-morrow—not just for a day, like the people who don't care about Tiberius, and think the Blue Grotto is the only thing to see—but to stay for several days. Brown says one could find a new walk on the island for every day of a whole month, and each would be absolutely different from the other, though Capri is only three and a half miles long and about a mile and a half in width.

I feel as if we were in for something exciting, just as you feel, I suppose, when you are going to bring off a big *coup* "in the street."

Your Chip-of-the-old-Block,
MOLLY.

P.S.—I wouldn't post my Naples letter. I thought if I did, you might imagine that we and our car had been engulphed in the sea, unless you got the end of the adventure tacked on to the beginning; so this is to be a fat postscript. Yes, a gorged python of a postscript.

At first the dock people couldn't be persuaded that we seriously intended to take an automobile to the island of Capri; and when they realised that we were in earnest, they buzzed with excitement like swarming bees. Everyone directly or indirectly concerned argued at the top of his voice, and embroidered his arguments with gestures, nobody paying the slightest attention to anybody else. We didn't even ask permission to go on one of the big passenger steamers, for we knew it would be no use; but there's a little sea-chick of a thing called *La Sirena*, which plies back and forth every day with provisions, luggage, and passengers, to whom cheapness is an object. She was our prey; and as nobody had happened to make a law against transporting motor-cars, simply because nobody had ever thought of taking anything so abnormal since Tiberius used to send his chariots, we could not be restrained.

All the loafers in Naples collected on the quay, and I don't believe anything would have been done for us if Brown hadn't calmly begun to widen the gangway. He had suggested that I should go over in the morning with Aunt Mary on the North German Lloyd that takes the trippers (as he calls them) over for the Blue Grotto, and lunch. But I didn't see it in that light, for I wanted the adventure. Aunt Mary *didn't*

"I SAT ON THE WALL OF A TERRACE."

want it at any price, so she was packed off by herself; and when the Lightning Conductor slowly drove
the car on board the little *Sirena* I was by his side.
There was a moment of awestruck silence on the
quay; but when Brown had gently manœuvred
Balzac into position in a clear space on deck, the
murmurs of doubt and disapproval turned into a
burst of delighted wonder. Brown and I felt like
"variety" artistes being applauded for a clever turn,
and the appropriate thing would have been to bow
and kiss our hands.

But all this was nothing to what was in store for
us at the Grande Marina at Capri. If we had gone
in one of the bigger steamers, we should have had to
get the automobile into a small boat, or perhaps lash
it somehow on to two boats; but the *Sirena* is so
small that she can come up along the landing-place,
which was one reason why, after Brown had made
inquiries, he was willing to go with the fowls and
vegetables. The nearer we got to the island, the
more beautiful it looked, and as we came in Brown
was telling me things about Tiberius' palaces and
where they had stood, when suddenly a shout went
up from the quay. A group of stalwart women,
clustered together there, were laughing and pointing
at our car. They belonged to a race of Amazons
bred on Capri, whose daily work it is to land heavy
goods and carry trunks on their heads to the omnibuses and cabs in waiting at the end of the quay.
Before we were fairly in, they swooped like a pack of
wolves on the car, laughing and gabbling, and somehow
they and Brown landed it on the slippery little quay

The news that there was an automobile on the island must have flashed around by magic telegraph, for people—swarms of people, more than you would have thought could live on the whole of Capri—came running from everywhere to see us start. I should have been awfully amused if it hadn't been for one thing. Up there at the end of the quay, where we must pass, were half a dozen hotel omnibuses and a long rank of smart cabs, like victorias, with very pretty little horses, whose faces looked incredibly short—perhaps on account of their huge blinders. They had feathers on their heads, and their harness was ornamented with all kinds of strange devices in silver or brass. Sweet little pets they were, that you felt as if you might ask into your house to sit on the hearthrug; and when they saw Balzac they all began to snort and shiver and act as if they were going to faint. Their drivers—in hard, white hats something like our policemen's helmets—flew to the poor beasties' heads; and some laughed, and some looked anxious, some angry.

Evidently the little horses had lived an innocent, peaceful life for years on Capri, and had never heard of railways or steam rollers, much less automobiles. I was so sorry for them, and wished I hadn't been so headstrong, but had been guided by Brown when he advised me to leave Balzac at Naples. However, we couldn't abandon the car on the quay, so we got in and Brown started the motor. Oh, my goodness' every horse went into hysterics! Their drivers he'd them, and said things soothing or the reverse, according to their bringing-up, but the little things kicked and plunged and doubled up in knots, although Brown drove by as slowly and solemnly as the Dead March in *Saul*. I thought we should never get past, but when we did the worst was still to come, for we had a steep road to climb up the cliff, and in the distance several cab-horses were trotting down. I begged Brown to stop and let them go by, lest they should jump over into space, so he did; and it was all that he and the drivers of the cabs could do to get the poor horrified little animals past us at all. That experience was enough for me. Brown pointed up towards Anacapri, far, far above Capri proper, on a horn of the mountain, reached only by a narrow but splendidly engineered road winding like a piece of thin wood shaving, or by steep steps cut in the rock by the Phœnicians thousands of years ago. "No," said I sadly, "we'll never drive up to Anacapri on the automobile. I shan't use it once again while we're on the island, and all the horses had better be warned indoors when we go down to take the boat."

But it was a beautiful drive up from the quay to the town of Capri and our hotel. I couldn't help enjoying it a little, in spite of feeling like an incipient murderess. I believe if I'd been on the way to execution I would have enjoyed it. The road swept round to the left, ascending loop after loop, to a saddle of the island lying between two cliffs, crowned with the most picturesque ruins I ever saw. Everywhere you looked was a new picture, and oh! the delicious colour of sky, and sea, and the dove-grey of the cliffs! You can see next to nothing of the town till you come on it; then suddenly you are in a busy *piazza*, with an old palace or two and a beautiful tower, and everything characteristically Italian, even the sunshine, which is so vivid that it is like a *pool* of light. Here we made a great deal more excitement before we drove under an old archway and plunged down a steep, stone-paved street filled with gay little shops, and ending with the courtyard of our hotel.

I know you only came to Capri with the "trippers" to see the Blue Grotto, and I feel sorry for you, you poor Dad, because, though the Grotto is so strange and beautiful, it is the thing I care for least of all. Just think, you didn't even stay long enough to see the sunset turn the Faraglioni rocks to brilliant, beaten copper, standing up from clear depths of emerald, into which the clouds drop rose-leaves! You didn't go to the old grey Certosa, for if you had you would certainly have bought it and restored it to use as a sort of "occasional villa," like those nice heroes of Ouida's who say, "I believe, by the way, that is mine," when they are travelling with friends in yachts and pass magnificent palaces which they have quite forgotten on the shores of the Mediterranean or the Italian lakes. You didn't walk along a steep path about twelve inches wide, hanging over a dizzy precipice, to the Arco Naturale—and neither would I if it hadn't been for Brown. I was horribly afraid, but I was ashamed to let him see that, so I struggled along somehow, and it was glorious. We ended the walk by going down a great many steps cut in the rock to the grotto of Mitromania, where they used

to worship the sun-god and sacrifice living victims—
human beings sometimes. You can see the altar
still, and the trough where the blood used to run—
ugh! and the secret chambers where they kept the
victims.

We stayed a day and two nights in the town of
Capri, and should have stopped on till we were ready
to leave the island, for it is a charming hotel, with
a big garden and a ravishing view; but I got it into
my head that I wanted to walk up all the Phœnician
steps to Anacapri—there are about eight hundred
of them—instead of going up by a mere road, no
matter how beautiful. Of course, Aunt Mary was
consumed with no such mad ambition, and as she
had heard that to go up the steps was like walking
up a wall, she was afraid to have me try the ascent
alone; so I asked Brown to take me. We started
after breakfast; and to go up all the steps we first
had to descend to the very shore, near a palace of
Tiberius', which is buried under the sea with all its
treasures. Doesn't that sound like a fairy story?
Then we began going up and up, and we kept meeting peasant girls tripping gaily down in their rope
shoes, singing together like happy birds, not even
touching with their hands the loaded baskets on
their heads. They were so beautiful that they were
more like stage peasants than real ones. Their
eyes were great stars, and their clear, olive faces
were like cameos with a light shining through from
behind. They were dressed in the simplest cotton
dresses, but their pinks and blues and purples, put
on without any regard to artistic contrast, blended

together as exquisitely as flowers in a brilliant garden.

I tripped gaily, too, at first, but the sun grew hot and so did I. Still, on we went, up the face of the cliff, and with every interval for rest came a new and wonderful view. By-and-by we got up so high that the row boats on their way to the Blue Grotto looked like little water-beetles, with oars for legs; and though the waves were beating against the rocks, we could no longer see them; the water appeared as smooth as an endless sapphire floor polished for the sirens to dance on. It was all so entrancing that I didn't know I was almost getting a sunstroke; besides, who would think of sunstrokes in January, no matter how hot the weather? Brown remarked that my lips were pale, but I said I was only a little tired. In rather more than an hour we came to the top, which was Anacapri. My head ached, so we went into a restaurant place, which turned out to be very famous. I sat on the wall of a terrace looking over a sheer precipice a thousand feet high until I felt partly rested; then a handsome girl, evidently of Saracen blood, brought me delicious lemonade. We had started away to walk into the village of Anacapri, when everything began to swim before my eyes. Luckily we were close to a house. It was a little old domed white house with a long vine-covered pergola, and it said "Bella Vista" over the gateway. I had to lean on Brown's arm going in, and the last thing I remember was a kind-faced man hurrying to the door. The next thing I was in a big white bedroom, sparsely furnished and daintily neat

I had fainted and they had sent for a doctor. Presently he appeared, and afterwards I found out that he was quite a celebrity—the "Doctor Antonio" of Capri. He said it was the sun; I hadn't eaten enough breakfast, and I'd had a "heat-stroke"—not half so bad as a sun-stroke; still, I ought to rest.

I was quite willing to obey the prescription, for I was falling in love with the house, and longed to stay in it for days. The room I was in had four windows, each one looking out on a view that stay-at-home people would give hundreds of dollars to see; and it opened on to a lovely private terrace. Brown took a message "downstairs" to Capri, asking Aunt Mary to pack up and come to the Bella Vista, which she did, and we've been here for two days. I was quite well in a few hours, but I wouldn't have gone back to more conventional comforts for anything. Anacapri and our little house seem as if they were in the world on top of the clouds which Jack discovered when he climbed his beanstalk up into the sky. Why, the first morning when I waked here, and opened my glass door on to the terrace to look at the sea, and the umbrella pines, and the cypresses (which I seem to *hear*, as well as see, like sharp notes in music), four or five large white clouds got up from the terrace where they'd been sitting and sneaked past me through the door into the room, just like the cows which, I suppose, the gods kept on Olympus to milk for their ambrosia. And the sunsets, with Vesuvius set like a great conical amethyst in a blaze of ruby and topaz glory! It is something to come to Anacapri for. But at the Bella Vista we would not feed you on sunsets and cloud's milk alone. The little landlord and landlady cook and wait on us, and I never tasted daintier dishes than they "create."

There are more things than sunsets and pines and cypresses to see too. One takes walks all over the island. One goes to rival inns where rival beauties dance the tarantella, and vie in announcements that Tiberius amused himself by throwing victims in the sea from the exact site of their houses. Oh, everything is Tiberius here. He is regarded by the peasants as quite a modern person, whom you may meet in a dark night, if you haven't murmured a prayer before the lovely white virgin in her illuminated grotto of rock. Mothers say to their children, "If you do that, Tiberius will catch you"; and the English colony of Capri quarrel over the gentleman's character, on which there are differences of opinion.

The most beautiful house I ever saw in my life is set on the brow of the precipice at Anacapri; it is a dream-house; or else its owner rubbed a lamp, and a genie gave it to him. It is long and low and white, and filled with wonderful treasures which its possessor found under the sea—spoil of Tiberius' buried palaces. The floors are paved with mosaic of priceless coloured marble, which Tiberius brought from distant lands for himself; a red sphinx, which Tiberius imported from Egypt crouches on the marble wall, gazing over the cliffs and the sea; Tiberius' statues in marble and bronze line the arched, open-air corridors. There's nothing else like it in the

world in these days, and few men would be worthy
to have it and to live there; but I think, from what
I hear, that the man who does live there *is* worthy
of it all.

You will find a rose and a spray of jasmine in this
letter. I picked the rose for you, in the pergola, and
our landlady gave me the jasmine. I wish I could
send you more of the beauty of this magic island.

Your enchanted
MOLLY.

FROM JACK WINSTON TO LORD LANE

My dear Montie,

We are at Taormina! When I say that, I
want you to realise that we have arrived at the Most
Beautiful Place in the world. Nothing less than
capital letters can express it. We have had six
glorious days in Sicily, and it is fit that these wild
ramblings of mine with the Goddess should end
here amidst such scenes of loveliness that even the
imagination can conjure up nothing more exquisite.
For end these ramblings must; to be continued, as
I hope (but dare not expect), in a life-journey in
which I may wear my own name shared then by
her. It is through my dear, kind, little match
making mother that I trust this may be brought
about; for my pluck fails me when I think of confessing my imposture to the Goddess.

I told you in my letter from Rome that at the
hotel there I found a forwarded letter from the
mater, saying that on account of the continued rain
and cold she and the inevitable Barrows had determined to leave Rome suddenly and go to Naples,
perhaps to Sicily, in search of sunshine. She added
that she had been worried about me, as she had not

heard anything for weeks, from which it is clear that at least three letters have somehow miscarried— doubtless owing to her constant change of address and the carelessness of hotel people in forwarding. The worst of it is that I haven't been able to re- assure her mind, as she gave me no new address, but merely said that when she was settled she would wire. Of course, I gave the hall-porter at the "Grand" the most explicit directions as to where I was to be found, and tipped him well. The result is that on my arrival here in Taormina I found a telegram (sent on from Rome) to say that my mother and the Barrows will arrive here to-morrow to stay a week with Sir Evelyn Haines, an old friend of the mater's, who has, I believe, bought a deserted monastery and turned it into a fine house. To-morrow, then, my mother will be here; I shall tell her everything, throw myself on her mercy, and get her to make peace for me with the Goddess. That, at least, is my present plan. But who can tell how events may upset it?

Well, as you don't know Italy south of Naples, perhaps you'd like to hear something of our Sicilian adventures. Of adventures, in the strict sense, we have had less here than in other places. If I hadn't been certain that the country was quite safe as far as brigandage is concerned, I should not have been such a fool as to bring two ladies through it in a motor- car. But we have had, as I said, "six glorious days," and the Goddess and I are agreed that in many ways Sicily is the best thing we have done on our whole long tour.

We landed at Palermo, after a night passage in a comfortable boat from Naples, leaving one world-famous bay to enter another scarcely less beautiful. Rarely have I seen anything finer than Palermo and the group of mountains round it as we steamed in at sunrise on a white and gold morning. The ship goes alongside the quay, so there was no difficulty at all about landing the car. It was slung, and gently deposited on shore by the ship's crane, and we drove off on it at once to the Villa Igiea. Everything was new to me in Sicily, and I confess that the Igiea was a surprise. One has heard that Sicily is a hundred years behind the times, and that in accommodation the island is deficient. That cannot be said any longer. The Igiea is perfect. Miss Randolph reluctantly admitted that there is nothing better in America. In situation the house is unique, lying under the tall, pink Monte Pellegrino. It was built by the Sicilian millionaire Florio for a sanitorium, but never so used. It is a long building of honey-coloured stone, standing in an exquisite terraced garden that stretches along the sea, and actually overhangs it—a charmingly irregular garden, with many unexpected nooks, and sweet-smelling flowers, palms, and all kinds of sub-tropical plants, fountains playing in marble basins, and a huge, half-covered balcony, where everyone except insignificant *chauffeurs* assemble for tea. Altogether a gay and delightful place, and it is having the effect of bringing to the island a stream of rich and luxury-loving travellers.

From afar I saw Miss Randolph and Aunt Mary breakfasting on the big balcony; and they could not

have lingered long over their unpacking, for at ten
o'clock I had orders to be at the hotel door with the
Napier. I knew no more of Sicily than they did, but
it is my *métier* to keep up the reputation of a walking
encyclopædia; therefore, in the small watches of the
night, while the Goddess and her Aunt slept the sleep
of the just, I had poured over guide-books and fat
little volumes of Sicilian history. What I wasn't
prepared to tell them that heavenly morning about
Ulysses, Polyphemus, the omnipotent Roger, and
other persons of local interest, to say nothing of
the right buildings to be visited, was not worth
telling.

We ran along the shore, past harbours and basins
where strangely shaped boats lay at anchor on a
smooth, blue sea, with an elusive background of
shimmering, snowclad mountains; and in a street,
like a moving picture gallery, we made the acquaintance of those painted carts which are indigenous
to the island. Quaintly rudimentary as carts, these
extraordinary vehicles are remarkable as works of
art, and the Goddess did exactly what I expected
of her—wanted to buy one. With her usual quick
discrimination, she picked out a fine specimen, the
wheels, shafts, and underwork a mass of elaborate
wood-carving, richly coloured, the boldly painted
panels representing a victory of Roger's, attended
with great slaughter. The little horse was jingling
with bells, and almost overweighted with his towering scarlet plumes.

"I must have that," exclaimed my impulsive
Angel. "Please stop the car, Brown, and ask the

man how much he will sell it for, just as it stands—
harness and all, but not the horse."

The much-enduring Brown stopped, ran back,
hailed the owner of the cart, who was accompanied
by a dove-eyed wife and seven Saracenic children all
piled in anyhow on top of each other like parcels.
Never, probably, was a man more surprised than by
the question hurled at him, but Sicilians retain too
deep a strain of the oriental to show that they are
flustered. He said in a strange *patois* that his cart
was the pride and joy of the household; that it had
been decorated by the one man in Sicily who had
inherited the true art of historical cart-painting; that
it was one of the best on the island, and he had
expected it to remain an ornament to his family
unto the third and fourth generations, but that he
would part with it for the sum of one thousand lira.
I beat him down until, with tears in his magnificent
eyes, he consented to accept two-thirds, which really
was more than the cart was worth, or than he had
expected to get when he began to bargain. The
cart was Miss Randolph's, and later that day I
arranged about having it taken to pieces, boxed, and
sent to New York. She was delighted with her pur-
chase, and in such a radiant mood that she thought
everything and everyone she saw perfect, from the
men milking goats to the dramatically talented
gardien of the beautiful old red-domed San Giovanni
degli Eremiti, once a mosque.

The German Emperor is rather a hero of hers,
and when we left the car in the street and visited
the Palazzo Reale she was charmed to learn that he

had pronounced a view from a certain balcony the finest he had ever seen, resting his elbows on the iron railing and gazing out over the city for half an hour. It really was inspiring—the blue harbour and the ring of sparkling white mountains, but I'm not prepared to agree with the superlative. I put the view of Naples from St. Elmo ahead. When the Goddess came to see the Capella Palatina with its gem-like Arabo-Norman mosaics, she was moved almost to tears. "It is matchless; the most beautiful thing on earth!" she said. But afterwards I drove her (Aunt Mary you may take for granted) out four steep miles to Monreale, and it was well that she had saved a few adjectives. Not that she is a girl who scatters much small coin of this kind, but she has usually the right word when a thing does not go beyond words. When it does she says nothing, except with her eloquent eyes. But in the ancient cloisters of that old monastery I watched her face, and it was a study. I believe, though each carved capital on each column is different from the others, she could enumerate in order the quaint and intricate biblical designs. In one secluded and dusky corner there was the faint tinkle of a fountain—a wonderful fountain, very old, and copied from a still older Moorish memory, by some Arab who served his Norman conquerors. My beautiful girl was a picture as she stood gazing at it, leaning against a pillar, her white dress half in sunshine, half in shadow, her brown hair burnished to living gold.

For the modern part of Palermo she didn't much care; the crowded Corso Vittorio Emanuele; the

Quattro Canti, which is the Piccadilly Circus of the Sicilian capital, or even the cathedral. But she loved the Villa Giulia, which she was greatly surprised to find a garden, not knowing that all gardens are "villas" in Sicily; she and Aunt Mary went in alone, while I waited outside the gates in the car; but her beauty and pretty frock excited so much attention that she was quite embarrassed, and I reaped advantage from her discomfiture, being invited to act as guard in the Botanical Gardens. I begged for her Kodak there, to take a photo (ostensibly) of the big building devoted to lectures, but quietly waited until she had inadvertently "crossed my path." Then I snapped her.

We stayed in Palermo for three days, and even so had the barest glimpse of the place. If I have luck, and win Her forgiveness first, and then at last Herself, maybe we shall come again to Sicily together, lingering at all the places we are slighting now. But dare I dream of it?

On the fourth day we set out for a visit to one of the show places of the island Girgenti of the Temples. And now we began to understand why the millionaire Florio, with his four noble motor-cars panting in their stalls, has not been able to induce his friends to stock their Sicilian stables in the same way. We knew already that Italian roads were generally inferior to French ones; that it was comparatively difficult to buy petrol, especially *good* petrol, or *essence*, in Italy, and I loaded up the willing car with several reserve tins on leaving the Igiea; but of course I had had to take the state of the roads on hearsay. The surprise and interest of the crowd, even in Palermo, where Signor Florio often drives, warned us that not many ventured with "mechanically propelled vehicles" where we were about to venture, and I was a little dubious, though the Goddess was in the highest spirits and yearning for brigands. She had heard at the hotel of a very picturesque one who owned a lair in the mountains, and urged me to pay the chivalrous gentleman a morning call, but I was both obdurate and unbelieving.

We started; occasionally, as we progressed, it was necessary to ask the way. The peasants we passed on foot, on donkey back, or crowded into their painted carts, were so wrapped in wonder at sight of us that it was useless to shout at them without warning; they couldn't recover themselves in time to answer before we had sped by. So I adopted a method I have often found useful. I selected my man at a distance, singling him out from his companions, and pointing my finger straight at him as I approached. This excited his curiosity and riveted his attention; he was then able to reply when I demanded a direction.

From Palermo on the north to Girgenti on the south of the island is something over sixty miles the way we went—sixty miles of bad and up-and-down road. Sicily is poor, and it could not but be to its advantage if visitors came to it in larger numbers. I should say one of the first things they ought to do is to improve the roads, and make them decently passable for carriages, motor-cars, and bicycles. At present the plan of mending the roads is to dump down so much "metal," and leave the local traffic to grind it in. As everybody avoids it and there is little rain, there it stays, and in consequence patches of sharp, loose stones lie over the roads the year round. Steer with all the skill one can, it's impossible always to dodge the stones, and our tyres got a good punishment.

The interior of the island, though grandly impressive, is unusually bare, save for its wild flowers, the ancient forests having long since disappeared. Our road lay for a time along the sea, and then inland, always mounting up into the heart of the mountains, by long, green valleys and over desolate plateaux where flocks of sheep and goats grazed under the guardianship of wild-looking shepherds and fierce dogs, the latter violently resenting the intrusion of the car into their fastnesses. We saw few people on the road, and passed only the poorest villages; but we had brought an excellent luncheon which we ate by the roadside, we three (would it had been two!), alone in a wide and solitary landscape. A very few years ago such a journey as this across the interior of Sicily would have been highly dangerous on account of brigands. As it was we had scowls from dark-browed men whose horses took fright at us, but no such encounter as we had with the peasants in France. An Englishman at Palermo who has lived long in Sicily warned me that every Sicilian carries a gun, and said that in the wild interior they would very likely shoot at the automobile for the mere fun of the thing as they would

at any other strange beast that was new to them.
This wasn't encouraging to hear. But though we
met some truculent-looking fellows on the road, their
sentiments towards us seemed to be those of wonder
rather than animosity.

The sun was sinking in a haze of rose and gold
as we came to the crest of the long hill on which
stands the town of Girgenti, passed through it, and
coasted down to the Hotel des Temples. Beyond
the hotel, which stands isolated between the town
and the sea, we saw suddenly the great Temple of
Concord, a lonely and magnificent monument. It
affects the imagination as Stonehenge does when
you see it for the first time. The red rays of the
sun shone aslant upon its splendid amber-coloured
pillars and colossal pediments, revealing every detail
of the pure Doric architecture. When the smiling
Signor Gagliardi had received us and allotted rooms
to the party (the best in the house for the American
ladies on their automobile, and a little one for the
chauffeur), I strolled in the fragrant old garden, and
leaning on the balustrade by the ancient well of
carved stone, looked long over this wonderful plateau
above the sea, where once stood perhaps the finest
assemblage of Greek temples the world has ever
seen. Next morning we went down to see the
temples at close quarters. I had been warned that
the road would be too rough for an automobile; but
a gallant Napier which had passed through the forest
of the Landes and braved the dragon's teeth sown
on the roads of Sicily's fastnesses was not to be
dismayed by a few jolting miles. Everyone in the

hotel—English, American, German—came out to see us start, predicting that if we came back the car wouldn't, or if *it* came back, it would be—so to speak—over our dead bodies. Aunt Mary was so much impressed by these dark prophecies that she refused to accompany us, and engaged one of the odd little carriages from the ancient town of Girgenti bristling on the height above our hotel. Thus it came about that I had my Goddess to myself, and in her congenial company I hardly knew whether the road was rough or no. Certainly the good Napier did not complain, and as for the tyres, the roads of Central Sicily had made them callous.

I thought then that never was such a day in the memory of man; but several days have come and gone since—also with her, and a man's opinion changes. I knew that in the society of no one else would there have hovered such a glamour over the ruins of Greek glory. Five noble temples they are, my Montie, of which two are almost perfect; the others pathetic relics of past grandeur, with their heaped, fallen columns. There they stand—or lie prone with here and there a majestic pillar pointing skyward—in a stately row between the brilliant blue sea and the billowing flower-starred plain on the one side, the hills and the grim city, like a crow's nest, on the other. Their sandstone columns hold oyster and scallop shells from prehistoric ages, while here and there a broken vein of coralline stains the dun surface as if with blood. Below the towering temples are shimmering olive trees, silver-green as they quiver in the warm breeze, and on this day of ours a myriad budding almond-blossoms were breaking at their massive feet in rosy foam. All the ground was carpeted with yellow daisies, pimpernel, and iris, blue-grey as my lady's eyes. Together we pictured processions of men and maidens, white-robed, bearing urns and waving garlands of roses, chanting pæans in a slow ascent of the amber-hued temple steps. We also were in a mood to sing praises as we drove back to the friendly hotel in its high eyrie of garden.

In the afternoon, I am sorry to say, we went up into the town—it is a bleak and gruesome memory; and next day we had a hundred and twenty miles' drive to Catania, our faces turned towards Etna, the Queen of Sicily, which we had not yet seen, but longed to see. In view of the awful roads we were likely to encounter, I had asked the ladies if they would mind starting at seven. They were ready on the minute, and I think they were repaid by the beauty of the newly waked morning, bathed in diamond-dew, and pearly with sunrise.

Again we drove through strange country, sterile save for the crowding prickly pears with their leering green faces, tangled garlands of pink, wild geranium, and a blaze of poppies spreading over the meadow land like a running flame. We penetrated the heart of Sicily, wound through her undulating valleys, and were frowned on by her ruined robber-castles; but the towns were discouragingly squalid, for much of our way led through the sulphur-mine district.

The true interest of that day came when from afar off we descried twin mountains, each bearing a huddled town on its summit. My midnight studies warned me that they were Castrogiovanni and Calascibetta, and I had suggested to Miss Randolph on starting that even at the risk of having to drive to Catania in the dark, we should not miss a visit to Castrogiovanni. At Palermo she had bought Douglas Sladen's book, *In Sicily*, and Miss Lorimer's travel-romance, *By the Waters of Sicily*, so that she was already fired at the name of Castrogiovanni, and needed no persuasion from me to turn aside to scale the ancient rock-fortress that marks the very centre of Sicily. I am pretty sure that never before has a motor-car climbed that winding road, and I think the whole population turned out and ran at our heels as we drove slowly through the sombre, wind-swept, eagle-eyrie of a town. As it happened, the day was overcast, and scudding clouds drifted coldly across the mountain-top, showing us the reason for the great blue hoods that the men wear over their heads, their Saracenic faces peering out as from a cave. We alighted in the market-place, and leaned on the balustrade to see the tremendous view—all Sicily spread out below us, gleaming with opaline lights and shadows. Hundreds of people clustered curiously round us and watched with dark, lustrous eyes, as if we had been beings from another world. We tried to ignore all these silent watchers, who, Aunt Mary said, gave her "a creepy feeling in her spine," and gazed out over the tumbled mountains of Sicily.

Suddenly a shaft of sunlight broke through the clouds and descended to earth like a golden ladder. It was the signal for a transformation scene. The white mists coiling round us, disappeared; the clouds floated away before a breath of balmy wind, and the landscape lay bright and clear at our feet. Then "Oh! What is that?" exclaimed Miss Randolph. I followed the glance of her eyes, and far away there was a great white floating cone of pearl soaring up into the sky. Yes, it was Etna!

At Castrogiovanni there is no inn where a lady can stay, so when we had seen the view there was nothing more to keep us. I had stopped the motor when we left the car, and everyone crowded eagerly round us as the ladies mounted to their places. Their amazement when they saw me start the motor with one turn of the handle was immense. A kind of awed murmur went up from the crowd; and when, with a warning blast on the horn, I drove slowly through their parting ranks, circled round in the market-place, just avoiding a procession of masked Misericordia, and putting on speed, passed swiftly through the streets, with a great shout everyone started to run after the car. We distanced them easily (Miss Randolph imprudently showering pennies), and ran at a fair pace down the winding road that led to the valley. Looking up, we could see the terraces and every window of the houses alive with wondering heads. Castrogiovanni will remember for many a day the visit of the first motor-car to its historic heights.

Catania is, I think, memorable to Miss Randolph merely because she bought there at a tiny but famous shop incredible quantities of curious Sicilian amber, streaked green with sulphur, absolutely unique, and valued as a luck-bringer. She says that she has a "pocket-piece" for each one of her most intimate friends in New York. Judging by the provision made, the name of these intimates must be legion. Apart from her opinion, however, I humbly venture to think that Catania has its points, if only people stopped long enough to see them, which they don't, Catania being the Basle of Sicily— the place of departure for somewhere else. In our case the somewhere else was Syracuse.

Now the Goddess had been looking forward to Siracusa; I'm not sure that she was not by way of regarding her whole past as working slowly up to a sight of that place, since she had come to think of it. She had made up her royal mind to stop there some time, dreaming in the quarries where the seven thousand Greeks languished in captivity while the Siracusan beauties, under red umbrellas, derided or brazenly admired them. She had, so to speak, made a note of Dionysius' Ear, and the Greek and Roman theatres, and already she had bought a photograph of a strange, Dante-esque den in the rocks which resembled Hades and was called Paradise. She planned an excursion up the little river Anapo to see the papyrus, and the deep blue pool of jewelled fish at the source; and there were various drives and walks which, she thought, would keep her at the Villa Politi at least a week. But, on my part, I was equally determined that she should not stop an hour over the two days I had grudgingly allotted her. Not that I wasn't interested in Siracusa; I was, intensely, but I was and am a good deal more inter-

"THE GEM OF ALL IS THE ANCIENT GREEK THEATRE."

ested in her and the carrying out of my own secret plans, which can best be accomplished with the aid of a sympathetic mother. I wanted to reach Taormina as soon as possible, so as to be on the spot when the mater arrives. Naturally I did not openly oppose the will of a mere Brown against that of Brown's mistress. I merely hinted that there was said to be a good deal of white dust in Siracusa, and that it was hot. I also mentioned, inadvertently, that in some of the hotels there were mice. It was a blow to hear that Miss Randolph liked mice; but there was encouragement in Aunt Mary's "Oh!" of horror; and I lived in hope.

In order not to waste a moment, I turned the car aside on the way to Siracusa, and drove along a white road between olive-clad hills to the ancient Greek stronghold of Fort Euryelus, which once guarded the western extremity of that great table-land which was the splendid city of Siracusa. You, who know your Thucydides better than I do, are probably well up in all the thrilling events which took place there four hundred years before Christ; but the Goddess depended largely upon my lips for bread-crumbs of knowledge, and her awed interest in the perfectly preserved magazines for food, the subterranean galleries, and the secret sallyport betrayed to the enemy by a traitor, was pretty to see. From a tower of piled stones I pointed away towards Etna with Taormina at its feet and said, "There— there lies the beauty-spot of Sicily." Thus I got in my entering wedge.

It was four o'clock when we finally reached Siracusa,

but I took my lady and her aunt for a glimpse of
Arethusa's fountain in the town before driving them
into perhaps the most wonderful garden in the world
—the double garden of the Villa Politi. It is double
because the heights, on a level with the white bal-
conied hotel, bloom with flowers and billow with
waving olive trees; while down below, far below, lie
the haunted quarries, starry now in their tragic
shadows with the golden spheres of oranges. The
latomia forms a subterranean garden; when the
brilliant flower-beds above are scintillating with noon-
day heat, down there, under the orange trees with
their white blossoms, it is always cool and dim, with
a green light like a garden under the sea.

The quarry is deep, with sheer white walls over-
grown with ivy and purple bouganvillia. It is of
enormous extent, winding irregularly, crossed here and
there with a slight bridge, and the hotel stands on
the very edge. Far away lies Siracusa, a streak of
pearl against the deep indigo of the sea. We went
down into the latomia and wandered into its most
secret places. But when we came upon a pile of
skulls Aunt Mary beat a retreat. The ghosts of the
tortured Greeks haunted the place, she vowed, and
lest she should be lost in the labyrinth of the quarry,
she had to be escorted up to the world of mortals.

Next day we did most of the things that Miss
Randolph had set her heart on, but not all. My
alluring picture of Taormina consoled her for what
she had to miss, and she consented to be torn away
on the following morning.

Our drive to-day has been a scamper through

Paradise. The road we took wound through orange groves, the sea lay glittering below us, mountains towering above, each hill-top crested with a ruin which had crumbled to decay when the world was young. My Goddess said that she had never known how much truer than history mythology was until this magic morning. Why, we saw the stones that Polyphemus threw after Ulysses, and the scene of Acis' love, and always before us, beckoning us on, was the white, hovering cone of Etna.

At last we struck the little station of Giardini on the coast, the nearest to Taormina, which lies some hundreds of feet above on a high shoulder of the mountains. An exquisite road, engineered in gradual curves, winds upwards along the mountain breast, and as usual the Napier took it at an easy ten miles an hour, and could have done it faster if I had let her. The view grew fairer and fairer as we mounted, and the coast line disclosed itself to north and south. In some three miles we were at the gate of the town. Taormina is practically a long, straight street, at one end the Timeo, at the other the San Domenico. It is simply a Sicilian village, with its Norman fountain and its crumbling palaces, but with a history that goes back to Greece in its prime. Above rises on a splendid height the old Castello; further inland, and higher still, is the wild village of Mola peeping over the edge of a precipice that overhangs the valley. Twenty miles away floats the stately cone of Etna. It is a place of entrancing beauty, and the gem of it all is the ancient Greek theatre. I suppose that nowhere in the world have nature and the noblest art that ever adorned the earth combined in a more perfect picture.

The resting-place chosen by Miss Randolph is not out of that picture, but a part of it. For five hundred years it was a monastery. How well those good old monks knew how to do themselves! They laid out a fairy garden on a gracious headland above the sea, overlooking a panorama the most beautiful in Sicily. They planted it thick with orange and lemon trees and flowers as sweet as bloomed in Eden. Now the monks are banished, but the garden remains, and their old home (with its lovely cloisters, its long, dim corridors pannelled with painted saints, its tiled rooms and deep-set windows) opens hospitable doors to strangers.

Aunt Mary is delighted with the San Domenico, because a "real live prince" is her landlord. Even the Goddess says that it makes her feel more than ever that she is living in a fairy story. Now, if only the fairy godmother will come along to-morrow, and waving her wand over Brown, transform him into a worthier hero of that story, and soften the heart of the Princess! Do you think it will be so? In any event, it has done me good to write you this. If all goes well I'll wire. I don't think there's much sleep for me to-night. As soon as there's a chance that the mater can have arrived I shall go down to Santa Margherita, Sir Evelyn Haines' place, and have it out with her.

Your somewhat distracted but faithful friend,

JACK.

MISS SYBIL BARROW TO HER SCHOOL FRIEND, MISS MINNIE HOBSON, OF EDGBASTON, BIRMINGHAM

Santa Margherita,
Taormina, Sicily,
January 28.

My darling Min,—

You were a saucy girl to chaff me like that about the Honourable Mr. Winston. It didn't matter one bit to *me* whether we got to know him or not. Why should it? Even when he comes into the title he'll only be a viscount, and Lord Brighthelmston may live for *years*. It wasn't to meet him that we joined the viscountess, though I shouldn't wonder if she had something up her sleeve when she asked us to meet her in Cannes. Anyway, she'd taken a tremendous fancy to me. We got on awfully well together at first, but she needs a lot of living up to, and if she hadn't held a sort of *salon* everywhere we've been, with all kinds of swells, home-made and foreign, kootooing to her, and being introduced to us, I don't know but I should have persuaded Pa to drop the whole business long ago. She's a nice old lady, but sometimes, when you let yourself go, and are having a ripping time, she freezes up and looks at you as if you were some unknown species of animal

321

in the Zoo. That's what I mean when I say sne wants a lot of living up to; and more than once in the last two months or so I'd have given my boots if Pa and I hadn't bound ourselves to travel about with her, but had gone off on our own, with a courier, like that handsome one I sent you the snapshot of with the Yankee girl at Blois. Well, anyhow, it's all come to an end now; and she's introduced us to dozens of smart people, so there's nothing to regret.

Pa and I are going back to Naples to-morrow or the day after, and so home to England. Give me London! I'm dying for a good game of ping pong. I asked them to get it at the Grand Hotel in Rome, but the silly things didn't. Addie Johnson has written and asked me to a swell dance she's giving at the Kensington Town Hall; I hope we can get back in time; and I may be able to take a charming cavalier with me. But I'll tell you about him later. We've been having scenes of great excitement for the last few days, which have helped me to get through the time in Sicily, which otherwise would have been pretty slow, as I don't care for country, abroad or at home. Besides, the oranges and lemons keep falling on your head, and at night you have to throw gravel at the nightingales to keep the noisy creatures still. I collected some on purpose.

Well, I told you how vexed Lady B. was because "Jack," as she calls him, couldn't get to Cannes. He was always writing from different places and making excuses, till Pa said in his joking way, he'd bet that "Jack was up to some game of his own," and my lady didn't like that a little bit. Finally, when Pa

and I got sick of Cannes, which is too far from
Monte Carlo to be lively, we all went on to Rome.
That was just after my last epistle to you. It rained
cats and dogs in Rome, and I never went into a
single church, not even St. Peter's. We planned to
wait for "Jack," but your letter came, and I was
afraid there might be something in that joke of yours
about his trying to keep out of my way, and I was
bound he shouldn't think I was after him. There's
as good fish in the sea as ever came out of it for
a girl who can bait her hook as I can. So when
Lady B.'s neuralgia got bad, we proposed Naples,
and it was very nice. But she is a fussy old thing
and couldn't let well alone; she'd seen Naples and
hadn't seen Sicily. Nothing would do but we should
"run over." I would have put my foot down on that,
but Lady B. mentioned that she had a friend at some
place called Taormina, an English baronet with a
lovely house, who always had a lot of nice people
staying with him. And she said she'd often been
invited, and would get an invitation for us all for
a few days if we'd go. I thought we might meet
someone it would be a good thing for us to know, so
I consented; but we were to go first to Palermo and
Siracusa, and work on to Taormina by the time our
invitation arrived.

Palermo wasn't so bad. I never saw so many
young men in my life, all very dark, with enormous
eyes, and little moustaches and canes, both of which
they twirled a good deal when they looked at anyone
they admired. But Syracuse was *awful*. I daresay
it was nice enough when you could be a tyrant and

cut off your enemies' heads, and build gold statues to yourself; but tyrants are out of their job now, and things have been allowed to go down a good deal since their day.   I nearly cried when I saw what sort of hole it was, but our invitation to Sir Evelyn Haines' (which we found waiting for us) wasn't for that day, but the next.   It was settled that we should go on by the first train in the morning, when a telegram arrived for Lady B.   She was in a twitter, and gave it to Pa to read, and say what he thought.   It was sent from Naples by a perfect stranger to her, who signed his name James Van Wyck Payne; and as nearly as I can remember, it said, "Beg that you will receive me at Syracuse.   Have travelled on from Rome on purpose immediately on learning your address.   Have news of vital importance to give you about your son."

Lady B. couldn't think what it all meant; but she was anxious, and we were curious.   She and Pa calculated times, and discovered that if we went away by the first train we would miss the mysterious Mr. Payne, so it was decided that we must wait till the next, and a telegram was sent to an address in Naples to that effect.

In the morning, as early as he could, he arrived.   I was on the verandah of the hotel, watching, dressed in my travelling frock, so as to be ready to get off by the next train.   When a stranger came running up the steps asking for Lady Brighthelmston, you can believe I kept my eyes open, though I pretended to be reading an awfully exciting book of Guy Booth-by's—really *great!*   He was young, and evidently

American, but very handsome, and the best of form;
blond, tall, and smooth-faced, with such a clever
expression, and *unfathomable* eyes. He was shown
in; but as Lady B.'s sitting-room had a window
opening on the verandah, with the blinds only half
shut, I could presently hear from where I sat a
murmur of voices which I knew to be hers and his.
Just as Pa had joined me, and was asking whether
the gentleman had turned up yet, there came a stifled
shriek from Lady B.'s room. We jumped up, rushed
to the window, and met her there as she was running
out to call us, crying, with Mr. Payne at her back.
We went in, and she made him tell his story, which
was very complicated. However, we soon understood that the Honourable Mr. Winston's *chauffeur*
had stolen his motor-car, and his watch (which Mr.
Payne had got out of pawn and shown to Lady B.)
and his clothes, and probably murdered him. Lady
B. hadn't had any letter for ages; she had supposed
that was because she was travelling about so much
lately and had missed them, but now she saw that
anything might easily have happened to her son.
Everything was frightfully confused and exciting,
and while Pa tried to soothe Lady B., Mr. Payne
and I stepped out on the verandah to talk things
over quietly, as I had kept my head. He showed
wonderful detective gifts, and from some details he
told me about the girl and a middle-aged American
lady, friends of his, whom the *chauffeur* had deceived,
I began to think it might be the party I had seen in
Blois, only with a different car; but that, as I said to
Mr. Payne, must have been before any tragedy had

taken place. He thought I was probably right about the identity; and to make sure, I went upstairs to one of my boxes which wasn't locked yet, and rooted out the negative of that snapshot I sent you from Blois. We looked at the film together, each holding it with one hand to keep it from curling, and Mr. Payne exclaimed, "That's the man! that's the scoundrel!" I had thought the face awfully good-looking, but it didn't seem the same to me then, and I had to admit it *might* be that of a murderer. I proposed showing it to Lady B., but she was frightfully upset already; and Mr. Payne said he didn't see that it would do any good to harrow up her feelings still more now, and perhaps if we did she wouldn't be able to undertake a journey. If he'd known in time that we were going on to Taormina, he wouldn't have kept us at Syracuse, but would have joined us at Taormina; for he had news that Miss Randolph, that stuck-up American girl, and her aunt had just arrived there the night before, with poor Mr. Winston's stolen car, which the wicked *chauffeur* was driving. He—Mr. Payne, I mean—had written from Rome to the girl's father in New York, that she was in the power of an abandoned ruffian, and the father had started off to the rescue the very day after receiving the letter. He had cabled to Mr. Payne in Rome, and the message had been forwarded to Naples, but in that way they had missed each other, and Mr. Payne only knew that the old man had been following the girl about from pillar to post; that he'd heard in Naples that she'd gone to Palermo, and had proceeded there himself.

Probably, when he found that she had left, if the hotel people could tell him where she was likely to be by this time, he wouldn't wait for an ordinary train, but would take a special. Mr. Payne said he was that kind of man; and if Lady B. would go on now by the next train to Taormina, everybody might confront the *chauffeur* and denounce him at once. By everybody he meant himself, Lady B., and this Mr. Randolph, of New York. I was very much interested, of course, and naturally wanted to be in at the death, which Mr. Payne seemed quite pleased to have me do, for we had by this time made up great friends; we seemed so congenial in many ways, and he knows such quantities of swell people everywhere. The Duke of Burford is a great chum of his, and so is that handsome Lord Lane that you were wild to meet last year and couldn't get to know. But perhaps you *shall* yet, dear. Who can tell?

Poor Lady B. was as weak as a rag, but determined on revenge, and Pa kept her up on a raw egg in wine. We took the train for Taormina. It was a strange journey. We four reserved a carriage for ourselves, and Lady B. asked questions till she was too exhausted to speak. Then she sat with her eyes shut, and salts to her nose, trying to strengthen herself for what was to come, while Mr. Payne and I talked in low voices about people we knew. Sometimes I *intimated* I knew them, too, and others still more swell, for I didn't like to seem out of it; and luckily I'd read a great deal about them in the Society papers, so I was never at a loss.

Mr. Payne was in communication with the American girl's aunt, who was partly in his confidence; and he knew from her that they would be at the San Domenico, at Taormina.   It was afternoon when we arrived, and as we didn't want to waste a moment, we drove past the very house where we were invited to stay, up to the San Domenico, where the wretched pretender was to be run to earth.   It was a very long, mountainous drive, and Lady B. was trembling with excitement.   She wanted to have it out of the man what he had done with her son, and, I do believe, if it had been back in old times, she would have been in a mood to put out his eyes with red-hot irons, or flay him alive to make him confess.   She didn't say much, but her eyes were bright, and there was such a flush of excitement on her face that she looked quite pretty and almost young.

At last we got up to the hotel, and had to walk through two courtyards; for it used to be a monastery, and is very quaintly built.   A porter walked up to see what we wanted, and Mr. Payne asked for Miss Randolph and Miss Kedison.   The man said they had gone out on donkeys for an excursion up in the mountains to a place called Mola, which we could see from the hotel, overhanging a precipice.   He said they hadn't been gone long, and probably wouldn't be back for at least two hours.   Then Mr. Payne inquired if their *chauffeur* who drove their motor-car was staying at the hotel, and if he had gone with the ladies.

The porter answered that the *chauffeur* was at another hotel, and that he had not joined the excursion, but he had seen the ladies off with their donkeys and guide. When the man began to understand that we were all more interested in the whereabouts of the *chauffeur* than of the mistresses, he added that one of the servants of the hotel who had just been down to the station had mentioned meeting the *chauffeur* in very smart clothes (quite different from when he had been with the ladies) going down the hill towards Santa Margherita, Sir Evelyn Haines' house, where there was a big reception on.

While we were talking another man came out—a sort of under-porter, and when he heard our porter telling that Miss Randolph had gone up to Mola, he said in that case he had made a great mistake, for he had sent an American gentleman who had been inquiring for her to the wrong place. He had supposed that she would be at Sir Evelyn Haines' house, for a bazaar was being held there for the benefit of a charity, and almost all the English and Americans at the hotel San Domenico and the other Taormina hotels had gone to it. The gentleman seemed in a great hurry, the porter had noticed; and he had said that he had come from Palermo in a special train, so as not to waste any time.

"Ah, didn't I tell you what Chauncey Randolph would do?" exclaimed Mr. Payne, turning to me as if we were old friends. I believe Chauncey Randolph has the reputation of being a millionaire; but I don't suppose he's got any more money or is a bit more important than Pa.

We had kept our cab, which was waiting outside, and after a few minutes' discussion between Lady B. and Mr. Payne, it was decided that we should drive straight down to Sir Evelyn Haines', where probably the horrible *chauffeur* was audaciously passing himself off as the Honourable Jack Winston, whom Sir Evelyn had never met.

Just as Pa was helping Lady B. into a cab, Mr. Payne exclaimed "Molly!" and I looked over my shoulder to see the stuck-up thing I had met in Blois. She was dressed differently, but I recognized her at once. I suppose some people would call her pretty, but I don't in the least, though she may be the sort of girl men like. She was walking, and her fat aunt was hanging on to her arm, and an Italian man leading two donkeys was close behind them.

"Why, Jimmy!" she answered, appearing to be very surprised, and glancing from Mr. Payne to Lady B., from her to Pa and me. She shook hands, then walked up to the cab to speak to Lady B., and had begun explaining that her aunt had had a fall off the donkey she was riding, and they had given up their excursion, when Mr. Payne interrupted her to do a little explaining on *his* side.

She stood looking perfectly dazed, as he told her how it was now proved beyond a doubt that her *chauffeur*, of whom she thought so highly, was a fraudulent villain, a thief, and, it was to be feared, even worse. He said that he had suspected for some time, but now his suspicions were confirmed by Lady Brighthelmston, who believed that some terrible evil had fallen upon her son through this Brown. Miss Kedison chimed in, and so did Lady B., and I don't much wonder that it took the girl some time to understand what they were all driving at, sharp as

these Yankee women are. When it was clear what
they accused the *chauffeur* of doing, she said it was
absolutely impossible, that there was certainly some
extraordinary mistake, and she would not believe
any harm of Brown. Then Mr. Payne told her that
anyhow her father believed, and owing to a warning
letter, had come all the way from New York to take
her from the clutches of an unscrupulous scoundrel
capable of anything. She *was* surprised at that.
Evidently her father hadn't let her know he was
coming. Perhaps he thought that if he did, she'd
elope with the *chauffeur*. She had gone from red to
white, from white to red, while the three poured
accusations on her favourite; but when she heard her
father was actually on the spot, she really *did* look
rather handsome for a moment. It was as if a light
from inside illuminated her face. "Dad *here!*" she
exclaimed, with her eyes shining. "Oh, then everything will be all right! Where—where is he?"

"Gone down to look for you at the house of Lady
Brighthelmston's friend, Sir Evelyn Haines, where
your *chauffeur* is swaggering about like a wolf in
sheep's clothing to be presently delivered into our
hands," replied Mr. Payne solemnly. "Come with
us, meet your father, and be convinced with your
own eyes of that scoundrel's guilt."

"If my father is there looking for me, I will go,"
said the girl. "Aunt Mary, you had better stay here
and lie down."

That is the way these American girls order their
middle-aged relatives about. If I told Pa to stop
somewhere and lie down, he'd tell me to go hang,

but Aunt Mary didn't seem to mind. She just bowed to everybody and trotted away, as meek as a fat white lamb, and Mr. Payne engaged another cab for Miss Randolph and himself, and we drove down the hill. Those two were in front of us, and I could see him talking to her all the way like a father-confessor, his face close to her ear; but she never looked round at him once.

I was almost as much excited as Lady B. by the time we stopped at the gate of Sir Evelyn Haines' house, which used to be a monastery. Most things in Sicily seem to have been monasteries or palaces. Our luggage had been sent straight up there from the railway station in another cab, for owing to Lady B.'s state of mind at Syracuse, no word had been sent as to what train we would arrive by. You don't drive in, for it isn't a modern gentleman's place at all, but has been left as much as possible as it was in old, old days. We walked, Lady B. leaning on Pa's arm, I by her other side, and Mr. Payne behind us with Miss Randolph, because she wouldn't go ahead, though I know he wanted to.

It's really a beautiful place, for people who like that old-fashioned, queer kind of thing, with a lovely garden, full of all kinds of flowers such as you see at home, and quite tropical ones, too. There were a great many well-dressed people walking about, for the charity bazaar was on, and no doubt everybody was glad of a chance to get into the house and talk about it afterwards as if they knew Sir Evelyn and had been his guests. There were tables set out under the trees, and tea was being carried round.

Suddenly I heard Miss Randolph exclaim, "There's Dad!" and at the same moment she ran ahead of us, across the grass to where a tall, big man with short, curly grey hair and a smooth-shaven face stood under a tree talking to another man whose back—which was turned to us—looked a tiny bit familiar.

At once Mr. Payne stepped forward, and said eagerly, "Lady Brighthelmston, the man Brown is here. He has got hold of Miss Randolph's father. Heaven knows what may have passed. Come with me, and confront him with a question about your son."

With a sort of gasp the poor old lady allowed herself to be hurried across the lawn, and I begged Pa to come along quick, because I didn't want to miss Mr. Payne's great moment.

Miss Randolph had got to the tall, grey-haired man, and was holding out her hands, without a word, when Mr. Payne said in a sharp voice, "Brown!" The other man turned. It was the courier I snap-shotted in Blois.

"Jack!" cried Lady B. And then it was our turn to be surprised.

We supposed at first that she'd gone mad; but, my dear girl, it was *true*. The murderous *chauffeur* was the Honourable Jack! But I do believe he was ashamed of himself for the silly trick he'd played, for all he laughed and showed his white teeth, because he was as red as a beet through his brown skin, and pulled his moustache, trying to talk, when his mother interrupted him by exclaiming, and asking questions which she never gave him a chance to answer. And while he talked to his mother, attempting to brazen it out, he looked at Miss Randolph, but she kept her head turned away.

As for poor Mr. Payne, I was sorry for him. He had meant so well, and worked so hard for everybody's good, and now it had come to nothing. He did his best to make himself right with his American friend, saying, "Mr. Randolph, at all events, this man has insulted your daughter, travelling around Europe with her under false pretences. What do you intend to do about it?"

But the big man answered, in a slow, drawling way, as if he were just ready to laugh, "Well, I guess I won't do much. Mr. Winston and I met here accidentally, and talked to each other awhile before either of us knew who the other was; and when we did know, why, he was able to give me a pretty satisfactory explanation. I guess there's nothing much that's wrong; and I hope Mr. Winston will introduce me to his mother."

Aren't Americans queer? I will say, though, that the girl didn't seem inclined to take things so calmly. Her cheeks were scarlet, and her eyes looked about twice too big for her face with anger or something like it.

Pa and I were rather out of the "durbah," for like the bat in the fable, we were neither bird nor beast, and had to stand aside while the fight between the two kinds of creatures went on. By-and-by Mr. Payne joined us, poor fellow, and I did what I could to console him, telling him that was always the way in this world, with the well-meaning, unselfish people. He was awfully grateful for my kindness, and when he heard that Pa and I had just that very minute been talking things over and deciding we'd had enough of being abroad, he asked if we'd mind his travelling with us as far as England, where he might stop for a few weeks, and drive about in his motor-car. Of course, I said we wouldn't mind; so I *may* bring him to the dance at Kensington Town Hall, if he isn't too big a swell for that set.

Of course, Sir Evelyn Haines soon found us out, and was very kind; but Mr. Payne would go, and I've hardly seen anything of Lady B. since, though it's now after dinner. I suppose the Honourable Jack is by way of being in love with Miss Randolph, or else he wants her dollars, which is most likely, considering the foxy way he seems to have gone about the business. But these American girls think such a lot of themselves, that they don't like being played with; and judging by the look on her face this afternoon when she heard the truth, she was hurt and angry all the way down to the quick. I shouldn't wonder if she refused to have anything more to do with him, for all he seemed to have got on the soft side of her father; and I must say, in my opinion, it would serve him right if she did.

Good-bye, my child. It's late, and I'm tired. I don't care a rap how the thing does turn out. It isn't *my* business.

Your affectionate

SYB.

MOLLY RANDOLPH TO HERSELF

January 28, HOTEL SAN DOMENICO,
TAORMINA.

I'm going to write it all down just as it happened,
and see how it looks in black and white. Then perhaps I can judge better whether I've been very
weak and undignified, and a lot of other things
which I've always been sure I never would be, under
any provocation; or whether I've done what no normal girl could help doing.

It's the sort of thing one couldn't possibly tell
anybody, not even one's dearest school-friend. I did
promise Elise Astley that if I ever got engaged, she
should be told exactly what He said, and what I said,
but then I didn't know how differently one would
feel about it afterwards; besides, I'm *not* engaged.
I only—no, this isn't the way I meant to begin. I
am afraid I'm getting a good deal mixed. I must
be—more concise.

Note 1. If I think when I come to read this over
that I have not demeaned myself like a self-respecting, patriotic American girl, I will tear this up and
write a letter to—a Certain Person.

Note 2. If, on the contrary, I decide, on mature
deliberation, that I could not have acted otherwise,
I will keep this always in the secret drawer of my

writing-desk, where I can take it out and look at it
at least once every year until I am an old woman—
ever so much older than Aunt Mary.

When Jimmy Payne suddenly hurled himself at
me out of a cab (just as Aunt Mary and I and a
donkey were trailing disconsolately down from Mola)
and exploded into fireworks calculated to blow my
poor Lightning Conductor into fragments, I threw
cold water on his Roman candles and rockets.

All the same, though, I felt as if I had been dipped
first into boiling hot, then freezing cold water myself.
I couldn't, wouldn't and shouldn't believe any of
Jimmy's sensational accusations of Brown, and I de-
fended him whenever Jimmy would let me get in a
word edgewise. But when he told me that Dad had
come half across the world from New York to Sicily
on the strength of his statements, I was *wild*—partly
with anger and partly with anxiety to see my dear
old Angel "immediately if not sooner."

I don't remember a word Jimmy said to me, driving down to Sir Edward Haines', where Dad had
gone expecting to find me. I've just a hazy recollection of being hurried through a beautiful garden;
I knew that poor Lady Brighthelmston (piteously
worried about her son) and a rather common girl
and her father, whom we'd stumbled across in Blois,
were with us. Their cab had come behind ours. I
saw Dad in the distance, talking to Brown, who
looked less like a hired *chauffeur* than ever, and then
—then came the thunderbolt.

It was almost as difficult to believe at first that
he had tricked me by pretending to be Brown, when

he was really Mr. Winston, as it would have been to believe Jimmy Payne's penny-dreadful stories. But you can't go on doubting when a virtuous old lady claims a man as her own son. I had to accept the fact that he was Jack Winston.

For an instant I felt as if it were a play, and I were some one in the audience, looking on. It didn't seem real, or to have anything to do with me. Then I caught his eyes. They were saying, "Do forgive me"; and with that I realized how much there was to forgive. He had made me behave like a perfect little fool, giving him good advice and tips—actually *tips !*—telling him (or very nearly) that he was "quite like a gentleman," and hundreds of other outrageous things which all rushed into my mind, as they say your whole past life does when you are drowning.

I gave him a glance—quite a short one, because I could hardly look him in the face, thinking of those tips and other things.

Then I turned away, and began talking to Dad; but very likely I talked great nonsense, for I hadn't the least idea what I was saying, except that I kept exclaiming the same five words over and over, like a phonograph doll: "I *am* glad to see you! I *am* glad to see you!"

Perhaps I had presence of mind enough to invite the dear thing to take a stroll with me, for the sake of escaping from Brown; for, anyway, I woke up from a sort of dream, to find myself walking into a summer-house alone with Dad.

"Don't you think," he was saying, "that you treated Mr. Winston rather rudely?"

"Rudely?" I repeated. "How has he treated *me*, I should like to know?"

"If you really would like to know," returned Dad, in that nice, calming way he has which, even when you are ruffled up, makes you feel like a kitty-cat being stroked, "I don't see, girlie dear, that you have so very much to complain of. I've been having a chat with him, and if he tells the truth, he appears to have served you pretty well. But perhaps you will say he doesn't tell the truth as to that?"

"Oh, he *served* me well enough—too well," said I. "But let's not speak of him. I want to talk about you."

"There's plenty of time for that," said Dad. "I've come to stay—for a while. Before we begin on me, let's thrash out this matter of Mr. Winston."

"It deserves to be thrashed," I remarked, trying to laugh. But I've heard things that sounded more like laughs than that. I hoped Dad didn't notice it was wobbly.

"He's told me the whole story," went on Dad, "so perhaps I'm in a position to judge better than you. Women are supposed to have no abstract sense of justice, but I thought my girl was different. You hear what Winston has got to say first, and then you can send him to the right-about if you please."

"I don't see anything abstract in that. It's purely personal," said I. "Mr. Winston can't expect me to hear him, or even to see him, again."

"He hopes, not expects, as a chap feels about going

to heaven," said Dad. "I'll fetch him, and you can get it over."

"Do nothing of the kind!" I exclaimed. "Let him stay with his mother."

"I guess I'm competent to entertain his mother for a few minutes," suggested Dad. "She's a very pleasant-looking lady."

I would have stopped him if I could; but when I saw he was determined, I just shut my lips tight, and let him go. What I meant to do was to whisk out as soon as his back was turned, so that when Mr. Winston should come, he would find me gone. There was no danger he wouldn't understand why; and a decided action like that on my part would settle everything for the future.

But as I got to the door I saw him, not six feet distant. He must either have been on the way to the summer-house when Dad left me, or else he'd been waiting close by. Anyhow, evidently he and Dad couldn't have said two words to each other; there hadn't been time; and there was Dad marching off as if to find and "entertain" Lady Brighthelmston. I should almost have had to push past Mr. Winston, if I'd persisted in escaping, which would have looked childish, so quickly I resolved to stand my ground—in the summer-house—and face it out. My heart was beating so fast I could hardly think, and I had to tell myself crossly, with a sort of mental shake, that after all *he* was the guilty one, not I, before I could catch at even a decent amount of *savoir faire.*

Naturally, as it was the only thing to be said, his

lips asked the same question his eyes had asked before. "Can you forgive me?"

I always thought Brown's voice one of the nicest things about him, unless perhaps his eyes; and both were at their very nicest now. I hadn't realized, till he came to me, how much I should *want* to forgive him. I did want to, awfully, but I felt it would never do; and I think I must have been commendably dignified as I answered: "The hardest possible thing for a woman to forgive a man is making her ridiculous."

"But then," he cut in, quite boldly, "I don't ask you to forgive me for a sin I haven't committed, only for those I have."

"You *have* made me ridiculous," I insisted.

"I fancied it was myself; but I didn't mind that, or anything else which gave me a chance of being near you, even under false pretences. It is for deceiving you that I ask to be forgiven. I lived a good many lies as Brown, but honestly, I believe I never told one. Do forgive me. I sha'n't be able to bear my life if you don't."

"I can't forgive you," I said again.

"Then punish me first and forgive me afterwards—very soon. I deserve that you should do both."

"I think you do deserve the first, but I don't quite see how or why you deserve the second."

"Because I worship you, and would rather be your servant than be king of a country in which you didn't live."

"Oh!" I couldn't say another word, for thinking of Brown being in love with me, and there being no

reason why I shouldn't let myself love him too—
except, of course, one's self-respect after all that had
happened. But just for an instant I didn't think about
that last part; and I was so surprised, and so happy
—or so shocked and so unhappy (I couldn't be sure
which; only, whatever the sensation was, it was very
violent), that I was speechless.

Brown took advantage of that, and talked a great
deal more.   I tried to look away from him, but I
simply couldn't. He held my eyes, and after he had
told me whole chapters about his thoughts and
feelings since the very first day of our meeting, it
occurred to me that he was holding my hands too
—both of them.   I am not sure he hadn't been
doing it for some time before I found out, but it
was his kissing the hands which brought me to
myself.

It seemed too extraordinary that Brown should be
doing that—almost as if I were dreaming. And to
be perfectly frank with myself, it was an exquisite
dream; because such strange things can happen in
dreams, and you don't seem to mind a bit. Luckily,
he didn't know this; and I snatched my hands away,
exclaiming: "Mr. Winston!"

"Don't call me that," he begged. "Call me Brown."

"But you are not Brown."

"I love you just as much as when I was Brown,
and more. If you only knew what thousands of times
I have longed to tell you, and the heavenly relief it
is to do it at last!"

"You have no more right now. Less, even; for
Brown *seemed* honest."

"If Brown had forgotten himself, and—and kissed the hem of your dress, what would you have done?"

"I—don't know," was my feeble answer.

"You would have sent him away."

"No—I don't think I could have done that. I—I depended on Brown so much. I used—to wonder how I should ever get on without him."

"Don't get on without him. I'll be your *chauffeur* all my days, if those are the only terms on which you'll take me back. But are there no other terms? What I want is—"

"What?" I couldn't resist asking when he paused.

"Everything!"

Something in his face, his eyes, his voice—his whole self, I suppose—carried me off my feet into deep water. I just let myself go, I was so frightfully happy. I knew now that I had been in love with Brown for months and had been miserable and restless because he was—only Brown.

I heard myself saying: "I do forgive you."

"And love me—a little?"

"No; not a little."

Then he caught me in his arms, though at any moment some one might have passed the summer-house door and seen us. He didn't think of that, apparently, and neither did I at the time. I thought only of Brown—Brown—Brown. There was nobody in the world but Brown.

I don't think I precisely said in so many words that I would be engaged to him, though he may have taken that for granted in the end; and if I did give a wrong impression, I had no time to correct it.

for it seemed that we had been talking about the future and such things no more than a minute, when Dad came sauntering by with Lady Brighthelmston.

They both looked at us as if they expected to hear something "extra special," as the newsboys say; and I gave a glance at Brown, or Jack, or whatever I ought to call him, which said, "If you dare!"

Having been forgiven once, I suppose he thought it would be wiser not to tempt Providence, so he held his peace, and we all talked about the weather and what a nice garden-party it was.

That is the reason why I still have the thing in my own hands. If I read this over, as I am now going to do, and disapprove of myself, it is not too late to change my mind.

P.S. I have read it. And I have thought things over.

Molly Randolph, if you hadn't forgiven Brown, you would have been a detestable little wretch, and you would never have forgiven *yourself*, for he is the best ever—except Dad.

It will be delicious to let myself love him as much as ever I like, at last—my Lightning Conductor!

THE END